Geologic Road Trips

IN GRANT COUNTY, WASHINGTON

Mark S. Amara and George E. Neff

THIRD EDITION

2003

MOSES LAKE MUSEUM AND ART CENTER MOSES LAKE, WASHINGTON 98837

Library of Congress Catalog Card Number: 96-83503

ISBN: 0-9649545-0-8

Cover photograph by Mark S. Amara, Milepost 26,
State Highway 243 north of Wanapum Dam

Cover and Page Design by Kathy Campbell
Printed by Gorham Printing, Rochester, Washington

Printed on acid-free paper

Contents

v PREFACE

vii ACKNOWLEDGMENTS

1 GENERAL GEOLOGY OF GRANT COUNTY

14 GRANT COUNTY ROAD MAP

15 INTRODUCTION TO GEOLOGIC ROAD TRIPS

TRIP 1 17 GRAND COULEE TO COULEE CITY—*State Highway 155*

TRIP 2 25 BANKS LAKE TO SOAP LAKE —*State Highway 17*

TRIP 3 35 CROWN POINT VISTA TO GRAND COULEE TO HARTLINE—*State Highway 174, Grand Coulee Hill Road, and County Roads R & V NE, 50 & 52 NE*

TRIP 4 38 COULEE CITY TO STRATFORD—*Pinto Ridge Road*

TRIP 5 43 COULEE CITY TO THE GRANT-LINCOLN COUNTY LINE— *U. S. Highway 2*

TRIP 6 45 SOAP LAKE TO MOSES LAKE TO EPHRATA— *State Highways 17, 28, & 282*

TRIP 7 51 SOAP LAKE TO THE GRANT-LINCOLN COUNTY LINE—*State Highway 28*

TRIP 8 55 STRATFORD ROAD TO MOSES LAKE

TRIP 9 57 EPHRATA TO QUINCY TO CRESCENT BAR—*State Highway 28*

TRIP 10 61 QUINCY TO GEORGE TO EPHRATA—*State Highways 281, 283, & 28*

TRIP 11 65 VANTAGE TO GEORGE TO MOSES LAKE TO THE GRANT-ADAMS COUNTY LINE—*Interstate Freeway 90*

TRIP 12 71 VANTAGE BRIDGE TO THE GRANT-ADAMS COUNTY LINE— *State Highway 26*

TRIP 13 75 MOSES LAKE TO THE GRANT-ADAMS COUNTY LINE—*State Highway 17*

TRIP 14 79 O'SULLIVAN DAM ROAD TO POTHOLES RESERVOIR—*State Highway 262*

TRIP 15 83 VANTAGE TO MATTAWA TO THE GRANT-ADAMS COUNTY LINE— *State Highways 243 & 24*

85 GLOSSARY OF FREQUENTLY USED GEOLOGIC TERMS

89 REFERENCES

91 INDEX

Location of Grant County, Washington

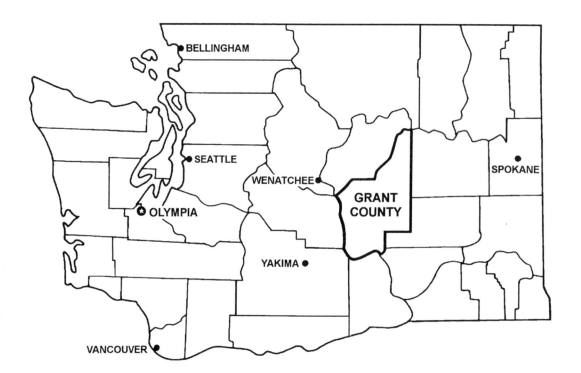

Preface

The impetus for this book arose out of a desire to provide a comprehensive guide and description of the rich geologic diversity that characterizes Grant County in central Washington. Users may consider one or more of the trips for guided tours, sites for outdoor classrooms, student projects, or as a casual travel guide.

The guide highlights the major geologic events, ancient environments, and sites to see while traveling freeways, highways, and other county roads. It is not meant to be all inclusive and the user may explore more or less as time permits. Each trip takes as long as the traveler wishes to sample the geologic landscapes identified in the guide.

More than 400 miles of federal and state highways and secondary roads are highlighted. Along any of the roads are superb opportunities to view the results of catastrophic events that have shaped the area and kindle the reader's interest in exploring the county. We hope that all who come to Grant County will see the extraordinary features described here as stark reminders of bygone times and as some of the most magnificent natural wonders of the world.

Acknowledgments

Several people supported and encouraged the development of this project. The initial idea was conceived when Mark Amara conducted volunteer geologic research for the Moses Lake Museum and Art Center in Moses Lake, Washington in the early 1990s. The idea evolved as Mark Amara and George Neff pooled their efforts and knowledge to assemble this special publication.

We thank the following people for their contributions:

Margaret S. Amara, Moses Lake, Washington, provided technical library support, ideas to promote the book, and helped review the text. Kelsey M. Amara, Moses Lake, Washington, contributed thoughtful illustrations and advice to enhance the cover. Margaret F. Amara, Portola Valley, California, was instrumental in suggesting avenues to publish the road trips.

Dave Clampitt, draftsman, Ephrata, Washington, completed technical diagrams used in the text. Nat Washington, historian, Ephrata, Washington, helped clarify and confirm several elements of local lore.

Barbara Guilland, Rebecca Powers, and Aleta Zak, Moses Lake Museum and Art Center, Moses Lake, Washington, used their copy editing skills to critique the manuscript, offering constructive recommendations for improving and strengthening it. Aleta helped prepare the final proof for the printer.

Ron and Darlene Johnson, Johnson Computer Services, Moses Lake, Washington, converted hand drawn maps and diagrams to computer generated files standardizing legends and improving readibility.

Joe Rogers and Murray Twelves, photographers, Moses Lake, Washington, donated their time to produce many of the photographs used throughout the book. Joe graciously edited the book helping to make it more reader friendly.

Teri Looney, artist, Moses Lake, Washington, provided artistic advice on enhancing the quality of the cover.

Ramon Cerna, graphic artist, Moses Lake, Washington, was an extemely valuable asset who donated the graphic art for the fifteen road maps, county map, other diagrams, and cover design. Ramon created visually appealing maps with his extraordinary artistic skill, giving the book a polished and professional look.

Chris Fiala Erlich, Director, Moses Lake Museum and Art Center 1992–1996, with the support of the city of Moses Lake, worked tirelessly with the authors to create and implement a plan for printing and promotion of the first edition.

Terry Mulkey, Museum Manager, Moses Lake Museum and Art Center in 1998 & 2003, with the generous support of the city of Moses Lake, coordinated efforts with the authors to promote and complete second and third printings.

Each of these individuals helped produce an outstanding final product.

—Mark S. Amara and George E. Neff

DIAGRAM 1—Geologic Column for Grant County

ERAS	PERIODS	EPOCHS	EVENTS
0-10,000 YEARS AGO	Quaternary	Holocene (recent)	★ Missoula floods Very large mammals Glaciers wax and wane
		Pleistocene	★ Cascade uplift causes arid climate
1 MILLION YEARS AGO			
	Tertiary	Pliocene	★ Structural basins collect sediments Cascade mountains form
		Miocene	★ Continued lava extrusions
Cenozoic		Oligocene	★ Basalt lava extrusions Forests thrive Temperate moist climate
		Eocene	Modern plants arrive
		Paleocene	Mammals dominate Mountains rise to north & east
70 MILLION YEARS AGO			
	Cretaceous		★ Deeply buried sediments altered to granite
Mesozoic	Jurassic		Birds arrive, modern fishes
	Triassic		Dinosaurs thrive
220 MILLION YEARS AGO			
	Permian Pennsylvanian Mississippian		Reptiles Amphibians develop Boney fishes
Paleozoic	Devonian Silurian Ordovician		Shallow seas Accumulating fine-grained sediments
	Cambrian		Early crustaceans
600 MILLION YEARS AGO			
Precambrian *85% of geologic time*			Worms and algae Widespread shallow-water environment

★ *Starred events show evidence in geologic strata at sites throughout Grant County*

General Geology of Grant County, Washington

Long ago, Grant County looked considerably different than it does today. Imagine a time millions of years ago when this part of Washington was covered by shallow inland seas. The seas disappeared as the area became landlocked, was filled in by sediments, rose above sea level, and became exposed to weathering and erosion.

Geologic time, in what is now Grant County, is represented by millions of years of incredible earth-shaping events which can now be interpreted from the natural record left by these events.

Geologic events took place over several hundred million years along with periods of intense mountain building, earth movement, and uplifts interspersed with long intervals of stability. Later, immense volumes of volcanic lava erupted and filled the Columbia Basin. Following this, a series of catastrophic floods barraged the Columbia River watershed over and over during the last 100,000 years. The flood events were repeated during at least three large-scale glacial advances and retreats.

Each flood event transformed and molded Grant County, and much of south central Washington, into its present shapes and forms. The magnitude of the changes created a unique blend of physical features that ranks among the wonders of the natural world. The impressive story of the geology in Grant County area is written indelibly into the landscape.

Grant County has innumerable places where one can visualize the extent of massive volumes of basalt lava flows that extruded onto the surface. These explosive events were succeeded by catastrophic flood erosion and deposition that occurred on a scale unmatched anywhere else on earth.

The authors hope that this presentation will enable its readers to appreciate the fascinating natural history that is unique to Grant County, Washington.

Granite Is Oldest Rock

The natural history of this area begins with the oldest geologic material in Grant County—granitic bedrock.

Granitic bedrock forms the base of the oldest geologic strata.

Near Grand Coulee, light gray granitic rocks are derived from the metamorphism of accumulated sediments (Neff, 1989). The rocks were metamorphosed (i.e., compressed under intense heat and pressure) around 65 million years ago (during the Cretaceous period—see DIAGRAM 1, GEOLOGIC COLUMN FOR GRANT COUNTY on page viii). Since that time these rocks were uplifted and eroded to form the Okanogan Highlands which extend from Grand Coulee Dam north into Canada.

The Great Basalt Lava Flows

Granite rock was buried under dozens of basalt lava flows that spread out like honey from a hot liquid lava zone that lies between the earth's core and its solid rock crust. Segments of the crust pulled apart, allowing the lava to rise and flow out onto the earth's surface depositing layer after layer. In some places accumulated thicknesses are thousands of feet.

Between 6 to17 million years ago (during Miocene times) basalt lava flows oozed out of fissures or cracks several miles long in the earth's crust and repeatedly covered Grant County. These fissures opened up as a result of two segments of the crust moving away from each other. Other fissures erupted intermittently into the Pasco Basin as late as two million years ago (Pliocene period) (Grolier and Bingham, 1978).

The lava flows poured out onto a weathered granitic surface of rolling hills, filling the lowest areas before lapping up higher onto surrounding highlands (McKee, 1972) and solidified into hard basalt rock. As the lava cooled, it shrank and created cracks in the rock mass, some of which formed the familiar columns characteristic of this type of lava rock. Lava extrusions piled up like layers in a cake.

More than 100 lava flows spread over portions of central and eastern Washington and into Idaho and Oregon, creating what is known as the Columbia Plateau. Grant County lies in the northwest portion of the Plateau. Accumulations of basalt vary from a few feet to more than 10,000 feet in thickness (Mackin and Carey, 1965; Schminke, 1964) though individual flows varied from only a few feet to hundreds of feet thick. This type of basalt lava is very fluid and tends to run like water, in contrast to the andesite lava of the Cascade Mountains that piles up around its vent.

After cooling and solidifying, basalt flows nearly always consist of a somewhat porous upper crust, a blocky mid-section, and a base made up of vertical elongated columns. These internal features are often mistaken as distinct flows. (DIAGRAM 2—PROFILE THROUGH A BASALT LAVA FLOW on page 3 can illustrate what to look for).

Individual basalt flows possess a variety of depositional and cooling characteristics that gave more or less resistance to flood erosion. Most basalt flows exhibit a classic three-tier profile. A vesicular crust formed as gas or steam bubbles were trapped in the solidifying lava flow. The entablature or mid-section consists of unorganized and blocky fracture patterns. In this central zone of the lava flow, liquidity was maintained and the liquid lava circulated internally even as the rock crystallized during cooling. The colonnade formed at the base of the lava flow. As the lava cooled, it shrank, forming cracks in a honeycomb pattern resulting in vertical polygon-shaped columns.

Some of the stable periods between basalt flow eruptions lasted hundreds or thousands of years. The evidence for these periods is seen in thick accumulations of sediments eroded from the surrounding non-basaltic highlands, fossil flora and fauna, and weathered rock that accumulated to form the Latah Formation.

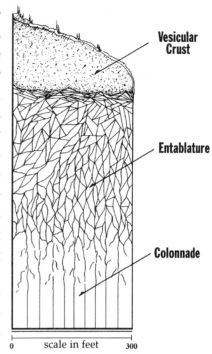

DIAGRAM 2—Profile through a basalt lava flow

Plants and animals are preserved as fossils in soils that accumulated between successive basalt lava flow eruptions.

Petrified trees are preserved in layers of sediment deposited between basalt flows or were encased within the molten lava flows. Several hundred species of petrified wood and fossil leaves have been exposed near Vantage (McKee, 1972) and are indicative of a forested landscape interspersed with lakes, streams, and marshes. The size of many of the petrified logs and the diversity of species represented indicates relatively long periods of stability between successive basalt flows. It also indicates much of the vegetation may have been transported in as driftwood from streams that originated in forested areas beyond the lava, thus accounting for the broad diversity of flora.

The Basalt Begins to Settle and Shift

The weight of thousands of feet of dense lava rock caused tremendous buckling and warping of the earth's crust throughout the Columbia Plateau. These tilted and fractured flows can be observed throughout the length of the Grand Coulee.

During and between the lava eruptions, varying rates of settling (called isostatic adjustment), caused by the tremendous weight of the basalt on the land, fractured the landscape as the underlying crustal rocks were pushed down by the load of lava flows on top of them. The lava flows near the margin of the lava plain tended to retain their original elevation because the lava cover was thin.

Elevation differences due to differential settling occurred on the Coulee Monocline (which the Grand Coulee follows between Coulee City and Soap Lake). Near Coulee City, the lava flows on the west (high) side of the monocline are thinner than those on the east (low) side.

Ridges such as the Saddle Mountains and Frenchman Hills did not settle as much as surrounding lower lands. These ridges were faulted and uplifted in response to the underlying adjustments in the crust and to the adjacent mountain building (orogeny) in the Cascade Mountains. Where the basalt is thinner on the margins of the Columbia Plateau, like the Beezley Hills (north of Ephrata) and portions of the Saddle Mountains (south of Royal City), isostatic adjustment had little effect, so these features remain close to their original elevations.

The crest of the Frenchman Hills created a vertical fracture zone along a hinge line, an active contact area separating the Pasco Basin to the south from the Quincy Basin to the north. As a consequence, the Pasco Basin settled more rapidly than that portion north of the Frenchman Hills. This differential settling caused instability along the hinge line so that a series of late lava eruptions along the east end of the Frenchman Hills flowed south from the Frenchman Hills into the Pasco Basin.

As the Columbia Basin warped and settled, explosive volcanic events and regional uplifts took place in the vicinity of the Cascades. Similar plate tectonic dynamics, often called continental drift, govern much of the volcanic and seismic activity in the world today.

Cascade Mountains Alter the Climate

Plate tectonic forces are responsible for the volcanic activity that created the Cascade Mountain range. The mountains rose in direct response to the continental plate and oceanic plate crunching against each other within the earth's crust.

The formation of the Cascade Mountains landscape began taking shape when volcanic vents opened up as much as 30 million years ago (Cenozoic era). Mountain building, erosion, weathering, leveling of the mountains (known as peneplaning), and uplift continued periodically with major volcanic episodes occurring during Oligocene and Miocene times (McKee, 1972). The Cascade Mountains continued rising to their present elevations in early Pliocene to Pleistocene times from 1 to 2 million years ago (Mackin and Carey, 1965) over the top of the older Cascade Mountain lavas. All the major peaks in the Cascade Mountains (and in fact all around the Pacific Rim, including Mt. Baker, Glacier Peak, Mt. Rainier, Mt. St. Helens, and Mt. Adams in Washington state) are the result of crustal movements forcing sections of crust into the fluid interior of the earth.

As the Cascade Mountain uplift and erosion continued into recent times, the impact of oceanic weather patterns on the area east of the Cascade range declined, resulting in the "rain shadow" effect that now causes the differences between western Washington and eastern Washington climates.

Before the uplift of the Cascade mountain range started, the climate of the Columbia Basin was humid and warm and had been influenced by winds blowing in from the Pacific Ocean. As the Cascade Mountains rose, the influence of the ocean became less dominant, the result being that the Columbia Basin turned more arid and the vegetation more drought tolerant. As ephemeral (intermittent) lakes dried up, the sediments became calcareous, resulting in white caliche (a type of limestone) being precipitated whenever soils or lake beds were subject to evaporation of water containing dissolved salt such as calcium carbonate. Locally, conditions changed from poorly drained or swampy bottom lands with low, moist swales and a diversity of trees, shrubs, and grasses in an area of low elevation, to well-drained bottom lands and arid slopes in an area of relatively high relief. Annual rainfall was gradually reduced from an average of 50 inches or more in the Miocene period to the present average of less than ten inches throughout most of Grant County (Smiley, 1963).

The Ancient Columbia River

The Columbia River drainage has been a dominant feature in the landscape for nearly 20 million years.

Over the last 17 million years, stream courses between the Spokane River and Wenatchee flowed westward and south following contact zones (Fecht et.al, 1987) between the basalt lava to the south and the ancient mountainous granitic terrain to the north. The ancestral Columbia River has flowed since at least middle Miocene times. Plateau basalt lava flows lapped onto the adjacent granitic terrain and dammed stream valleys to form lakes. Sediments collected in the lakes and were buried under the next overlapping lava flow to form the upper Miocene Latah Formation. Latah Formation sediments can be seen along the highway near the city of Grand Coulee. The Columbia River initially flowed atop the lava plateau but eventually cut down into it following the weak contact zone between the granitic and basaltic bedrock.

Hundreds of feet of fine-textured lake beds and stream deposits overlie basalt rock in Grant County.

The Columbia River and its tributaries, the Snake and Palouse Rivers, including Crab Creek, Lind Coulee, and Rocky Coulee in Grant County deposited hundreds of feet of sediments over the top of the basalt flows. These Ringold sediments, named for the White Bluffs exposures near Ringold, Washington, occur as lacustrine (lake sediments), finely bedded (layered) sands, silts, and clays and fluvial (stream) deposits. Fossils south of Othello in the Ringold Formation sediments have been dated between 3 and 8 million years old (Pliocene period). The climate was wetter than today with riparian areas, meadows, and rolling topography, with evidence of a diverse mammal population including bear, sloth, antelope, beaver, camel, and fish.

Beginning of the Ice Age

The arrival of the Ice Age (Pleistocene) found Grant County consisting of the Beezley Hills on the northwest, the Frenchman Hills through the middle, and the Saddle Mountains near the southern boundary. The Quincy Basin, the lower Crab Creek (Othello) Basin, and the Pasco Basin were filled with a combination of lake and wind-deposited sediments, and the upslope to the east was covered with loess (wind-deposited very fine sands and silts).

Ice ages are a result of persistent excess of snowfall over evaporation and melting over a large part of a continental land mass. The internal pressure of the glaciers converted snow into ice that initially spread out from high elevation locations like big globs of cold honey. Snow converted into ice continued to creep toward the margin of the ice. It spread out until it reached locations where the annual melting and evaporation dissipated the ice as fast as the center of accumulation could match the discharge.

Though glaciers advanced and withered away over the last 100,000 years, the geologic record suggests they did not directly enter Grant County.

Imagine a continuous glacial ice front (referred to as continental glaciers) moving south from Canada. The glaciers ranged on the west from Washington's coastal mountains and extended eastward through Douglas

County, across the southern parts of Okanogan, Ferry, Stevens, and Pend Orielle Counties in Washington, Kootenai County, Idaho, and into Montana and the Canadian Rockies. Grant County was miraculously spared by the glaciers. The southern margin of glacial ice reached the Grant County-Douglas County line along U. S. Highway 2 west of Coulee City.

There is evidence of at least three glacial advances and retreats during the last 100,000 years (Pleistocene). The latest retreat of the glaciers was less than 15,000 years ago (Mackin and Carey, 1965). Although Grant County was not directly touched by glacial ice, it was influenced by events occurring next to the glaciers (called periglacial phenomena).

The Great Ice Age Floods

There is overwhelming evidence that glacial meltwater, originating in Glacial Lake Missoula in western Montana, swept through the county on several occasions.

Similar types of flood events are known to have occurred in the upper Midwest and central Canada where Glacial Lake Agassiz overflowed into the Mississippi Valley. Temporary impoundments and ice age flood events have also been postulated for Siberia's Lake Baikal. Another area subject to infrequent large-scale flooding has been recognized in northern Australia where many of the basic hydraulic characteristics of the channeled scablands have been documented.

The earliest catastrophic floods are dated at more than 50,000 years ago. The floods partially scoured out the Cheney-Palouse scabland area east of Grant County and entered the Lind Coulee drainage (east of Warden) before emptying into the Quincy Basin. Floodwaters also spilled eastward out of the Columbia River over Babcock and Evergreen ridges near George and Quincy. Tens of thousands of years passed before flood deposits again left their marks. During this time interval, several feet of loessial soil covered the flood deposits, and caliche cemented the base of the soil and the top of the underlying gravel. Gravelly glacial outwash deposits south and west of Quincy and areas adjacent to George in the western part of the basin and along the Columbia River are the earliest flood deposits in Grant County (Gentry, 1984).

It is not known with certainty how many floods there were, but there were numerous opportunities for catastrophic discharges from Lake Missoula. Evidence of smaller floods were largely destroyed by the biggest flood that occurred during the period 14,000 to 18,000 years ago.

Geologic evidence suggests at least three major floods and perhaps several more occurred (Neff, 1989; Shelton, 1966). Physical evidence of a fourth flood that dramatically altered Grant County has recently been brought to light, though the actual number of flood events is still a controversial subject in the scientific community.

The flood events all originated from impounded waters in western Montana that repeatedly filled and emptied as the glaciers advanced and melted. Glacial ice is known to have blocked the Clark Fork River in Montana, holding behind it an estimated 500 cubic miles of water. When this ice dam broke, glacial meltwater raced across the North Idaho panhandle and fanned out down the Columbia River drainage and points southwest of Spokane. Glacial ice also dammed the Columbia River at Grand Coulee at the same time, forcing the meltwater to forge a new channel down Moses Coulee and south toward Soap Lake, Moses Lake, and the Drumheller Channels to flow back into the outlet by way of Crab Creek at Schawana.

During the maximum extent of the Cordilleran (continental) glacial ice sheet, ice dams blocked several rivers behind which accumulated large lakes with huge quantities of water. One of the largest of these ice-dammed lakes was Glacial Lake Missoula centered near Missoula, Montana. Visualize an ice dam, which crossed the Clark Fork River in the Cabinet Gorge east of Sandpoint near the Montana border. This dam held back an estimated 500 cubic miles of water. Perhaps a slowing down of the southward flow of glacial ice could have combined with melting ice in the natural dam that blocked the river to create ideal conditions for ice dam failure. When the impounded water rose against the ice dam to a level that would float the ice, it emerged from Lake Missoula. From there, the meltwater that produced the most devastating impact to Grant County, mixed with glacial ice, raced across the south central part of Washington, flooding all but the highest land. It is estimated that the water released from the failure of this dam was hundreds of feet deep and water flows were at least 60 times larger than the Amazon River.

The same series of flood events are known by various names: Missoula Floods, Spokane Floods, or the Bretz Floods.

The Missoula Floods are often called the Spokane Floods or Bretz Floods after J Harlen Bretz who first proposed the flood theory and supported it with physical evidence documented in publications between 1923 and 1978 (Neff, 1989). The alluvial deposits produced by the floods are the major source of sand, gravel, and boulders in Grant County.

The Grand Coulee gorge, between the cities of Grand Coulee and Soap Lake, was gouged and shaped into its present form in a matter of weeks by the largest flood on record. Flood deposits and eroded surfaces created by this event are the dominant physical features that make up Grant County today. The area affected by floodwaters is graphically illustrated in DIAGRAM 3—AREA AFFECTED BY GLACIAL LAKE MISSOULA FLOODING on page 10.

Passage of floodwater down the Columbia River was blocked by the Okanogan lobe of the Cordilleran (continental) ice sheet. Glaciers filled the Okanogan Valley and pushed southward onto the Waterville Plateau in Douglas County. As a result, floodwaters from Glacial Lake Missoula were forced to forge a route south creating the Grand Coulee. Before the upper Grand Coulee was completely excavated, the western margin of the flood skirted and overran the margin of the ice sheet to be diverted southwestward entering the Sagebrush Flats basin (northwest of Ephrata) and gouging out Moses Coulee into the Columbia River. Meanwhile back at Grand Coulee, the headward erosion of the upper Grand Coulee cataract grew to accommodate more and more of the flood. The flow into Moses Coulee was then pirated and the impoundment of water in Lake Columbia was tapped by the rapid removal of rock between Steamboat Rock and the Columbia Valley. From there, floodwaters burst south out of the Grand Coulee, across the Quincy Basin to cross from east to west over Babcock Ridge and Evergreen Ridge (west of Quincy) and into the Columbia River proper. At the same time it sculpted the Drumheller Channels in Crab Creek on its way to another Columbia River outlet. The effects of this great flood or floods were recent enough that its features have been covered by only a few inches of wind-transported and deposited (loess) soil and volcanic ash.

This largest burst of floodwater was the last great catastrophic flood in the central Columbia Basin (Neff, 1989; Fecht, et. al. 1987; Bretz, 1969). Water churned through the area quickly. The hydraulic characteristics at the maximum flood discharge are the product of a very fast moving torrent in which parameters were constantly changing (Neff, 1989).

Reliable estimates have been developed to assess the hydraulic characteristics of the numerous trains of giant ripples in the area ravaged by the floods including those in the Columbia River. Calculations (Baker, 1973) show that water depths must have ranged from 40 to 500 feet. Water surface slopes ranged from seven to 30 feet per mile and water flows may have reached 386 million cubic feet per second. Water velocity estimates showed that the size of material carried, sand to boulders in excess of five feet in diameter (Webster, et. al., 1976), was justifiable.

The "Grand Coulee" network of channels is a 50-mile-long trench

DIAGRAM 3—Area Affected by Glacial Lake Missoula Flooding

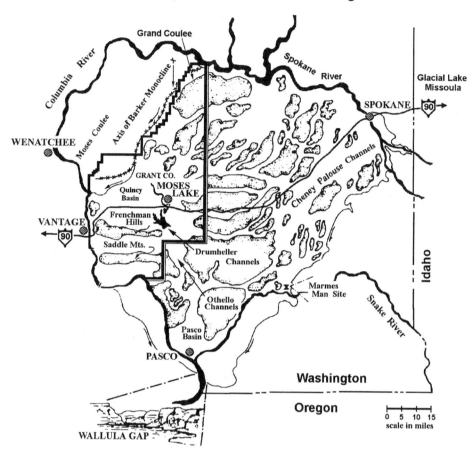

that displays catastrophic flood features formed as a result of these floods. Grand Coulee is the steepest, longest, deepest cut in the Columbia Plateau and has a higher number of abandoned cataracts and distributary canyons than anywhere else on the Plateau (Neff, 1989; Allen, et. al., 1986). The coulee system is a testament to the massive volume and power of water that swept through the area in relatively short-lived deluges.

This super-velocity water also gouged out the meanders in the surface of the land which form Moses Lake and put the final touches in the terraces present there today. A similar event is evident in the main channel of the Columbia River with characteristic gravel bars, ripple marks, and boulder-strewn surfaces.

The floods stripped away several hundred million years of bedrock and sediment and deposited hundreds of feet of sand, gravel, and boulders haphazardly over the landscape.

Even the highly resistant basalt lava flows were plucked and scoured away forming channels cut hundreds of feet deep into the basalt (Bretz, 1969). The resulting channeled scablands show the effect of the floods. Exposures at Soap Lake, Lake Lenore, Dry Falls, Moses Lake, the Drumheller Channels and the Columbia River Gorge are local examples of the catastrophic nature of the floods.

The flood process would have been remarkable to witness. The burst of water from Lake Missoula released a massive swath of water through central Washington. Incredible volumes of ice, rock, sand, silt and clay smashed through the Basin and out the Columbia River to the Pacific Ocean like an oversized tidal wave. Strong currents would have flushed through the area huge volumes of slurry; a soup-like mixture of mud, sand, rocks, and ice. As the velocity fluctuated or decreased along the sides of the channels, a wide array of depositional and erosional features were created. Depositional features including gigantic ripple marks, gravel bars, terraces, valley fills, fans, deltas, lake sediments, and natural levees are common all along the flood route. The remaining impounded waters may have taken weeks, months, or even years to disappear. Erosional features include scablands, dry falls, cliffs, depressions, and hanging valleys.

Icebergs dislodged and buoyed by the floods contained soil, rock, and rock flour that originated from as far away as the Canadian Rockies. This material was dropped on the ground when the water left and the ice melted.

Large pieces of glacial ice (icebergs) were also prevalent as the ice melted or broke up. Erratics, rocks not indigenous to the location and chunks of dislocated and frozen soil, rock, and rock flour (pulverized rock), were carried by icebergs and dropped by floodwaters. Erratics were of two types. Some erratics were dislodged from the granitic rocks that outcrop between Steamboat Rock and Grand Coulee (city) and were rolled or carried in suspension. Other erratics are ice-rafted boulders, which were contained in glacial ice picked up by glacial erosion in the American and Canadian Rockies and subsequently were stranded as the ice raft melted after the ice-laden floodwaters subsided. These boulders are composed of a wide variety of rocks characteristic of the Rocky Mountains including limestone, argillite, quartzite, and granite. The presence of ice-rafted boulders indicates that free-flowing water, traveling south from the glaciers, transported these materials and redeposited them throughout the Columbia Basin. Look for these erratic boulders in several places around Moses Lake and in other localities swept by the floods along the Columbia River drainage including Pasco, Portland and the Willamette Valley in Oregon. The erratics have been traced back to source areas in

Montana and Canada. These non-native rocks demonstrate the distances traveled, size and depth of the flood, and the enormous volumes of water and glacial ice.

Evidence of two more mini-floods prior to 10,000 years ago are recorded in the geologic record as erosional surfaces and bouldery landscapes on the edge of and in Grant County.

As the floodwaters from this largest catastrophic flood subsided, water ponded in the upper end of the Grand Coulee. South of Steamboat Rock to the city of Grand Coulee and northward, the lake called Lake Columbia refilled. Fine-bedded layers of sediment, called the Nespelem Formation, are several feet thick and may be seen in this area. Sometime more recently than 13,000 years ago, the water from Lake Columbia must have burst down the Grand Coulee and into the Columbia Basin, severely eroding the lake sediments leaving these beds dissected and fragmentary throughout the length of the Coulee. This burst of late glacial meltwater could have plucked out bouldery portions of highly fractured basalt lava flows near Soap Lake and deposited them on the surface of the floodplain between Soap Lake, Ephrata, and Moses Lake. The eroded steep-sided slopes or scarps along Crab Creek and Rocky Ford Creek are evidence of this last flush of floodwater. Eventually the water ran down the pre-existing flood channels and out to the Columbia River through the Drumheller Channels and lower Crab Creek.

An even more recent flood at 10,000 to 11,000 years ago was confined to the Columbia River channel. Erosion that removed or cut away a portion of the ripple-marked landscape on the margin of Crescent Bar is evidence of this latest event.

The repeated floods swept away all but a few scattered remnants of windblown silts called loess within their path in the central part of the Quincy Basin. Scattered patches of land left untouched by the floodwaters north and east of Moses Lake show accumulations of loess lying on top of the basalt. The Palouse region of southeastern Washington (where deep loess soils occur today) and the deep water-laid deposits of Ringold Formation clays, silts, and fine sands that escaped the flooding would have been similar to what Grant County looked like in pre-flood times before glacial meltwaters scoured away residual soils and rock and typically dropped tens of feet of sand and gravel.

Following each flood event, areas of central and south central Washington were covered by temporary ponding of floodwaters. Evidence of these lakes are recorded north and south of the Frenchman Hills, into the Quincy, Othello, Warden, and Pasco areas and throughout the length of the Grand Coulee and the Columbia Gorge. The Lind Coulee, known to have been a perennial spring-fed stream during this period, along with many adjacent streams (including Crab Creek and Rocky Ford Creek), probably fed these lakes.

Lakes drained and swelled between 10,000 and 14,000 years ago. Then they, too, became gradually smaller (Shelton, 1966). Where sustained by ground water emergence, the lakes never completely dried up. Interbedded in the lake sediments and in the overlying unconsolidated sediments are volcanic ash beds that are used as stratigraphic marker horizons that geologists use to date the deposits. Subsequent accumulations of sediments in the stream courses and windblown soil deposits including volcanic ash complete the generalized stratigraphic sequence for the region.

The Modern Era

No other natural events have significantly changed the landscape since the floods subsided. However, beginning in the 1950s irrigation water was diverted from the Columbia River to hundreds of thousands of acres, creating an oasis in the desert. The addition of surplus irrigation water to the ground water and streams of the area instituted a partial return of water abundance.

The Grant County landscape has been little altered over the last 10,000 years since the Missoula Floods. The availability of irrigation water through the Columbia Basin Irrigation Project in the 1950s has made water a plentiful commodity in an area where annual rainfall ranges from six to nine inches. The project was built for the purpose of providing water for agricultural irrigation on a million acres of semi-arid land. Grand Coulee Dam, completed in 1941, impounds the Columbia River and provides energy for pumping water from the reservoir into upper Grand Coulee where it is collected in Banks Lake. Banks Lake is the storage tank from which water is conveyed through a canal system and delivered to the land (Neff, 1989). Crops grown in the dry land outside the project area are limited to just a few like wheat or barley. In the irrigated portion of the Columbia Basin, however, more than seventy different crop types are currently grown. In addition, many irrigated farms on the periphery of the project pump ground water that is sustained by deep percolation of water from project-supplied farms.

Grant County Road Map

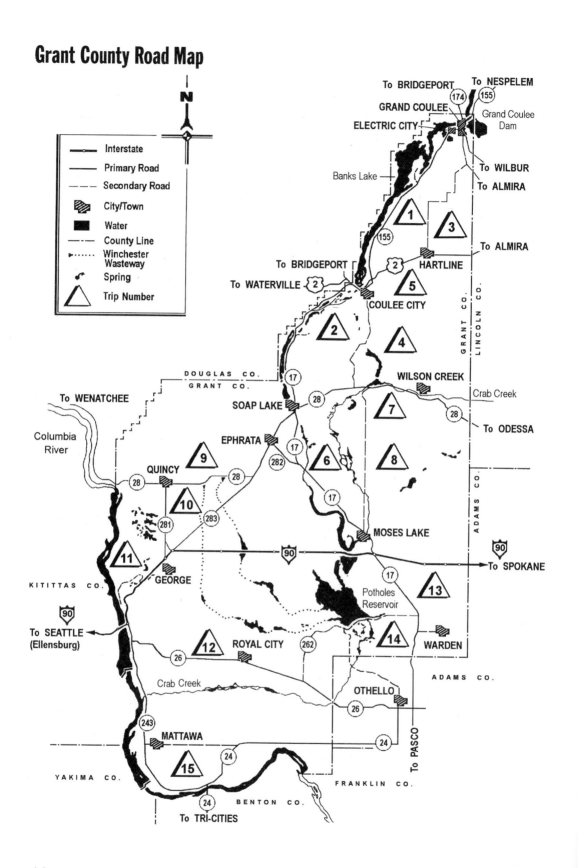

Introduction to Geologic Road Trips

This book is divided into two sections, a general geology section at the beginning followed by a series of detailed road trips. Though travelers are encouraged to read the section on the general geology first before proceeding to the road trips, it is not absolutely necessary and one section or the other section may be read without looking at the other.

The following fifteen trips are designed to help travelers see the geologic effects of the formation of Grant County and the subsequent man-made effects of irrigation on the landscape. Taken in order they go from the oldest geologic formations to the youngest.

An array of depositional and erosional features have transformed this part of Washington into a geologic wonderland unmatched anywhere else in the world. These events were so large and complex that they are difficult to perceive and almost defy description. Please bear with us while we try.

The road map of Grant County that precedes this section shows the principle tour routes followed. Each trip is preceded in the book by a map of that particular route. Most Grant County roads are identified by a grid system using 1-mile units on a coordinate grid with numerical sequences north and south and alphabetical designations east and west.

The trips in this guide are keyed to roadside markers found on freeways and highways. These milepost markers help locate the important features explained in the text. When, for example, the text identifies a marker labeled N MP 12 it means to look north of milepost 12. A marker labeled S MP 44 means the traveler should look south of milepost 44. A more general system has been used to approximate locations on the secondary routes.

It is easier to use the guide in sequence. However, it may be used in the reverse direction as long as the reader starts at the end of a section and works backwards.

The first trip listed starts at Grand Coulee near the northern border of Grant County. However, it may begin from whatever road the traveler is entering from by keying in on milepost markers identified in the text.

Use turnouts as much as possible. Where that is not practical, pull as far off the road as possible.

Come anytime and have a good trip.

Milepost marker

Grand Coulee to Coulee City

Approx. 25 miles

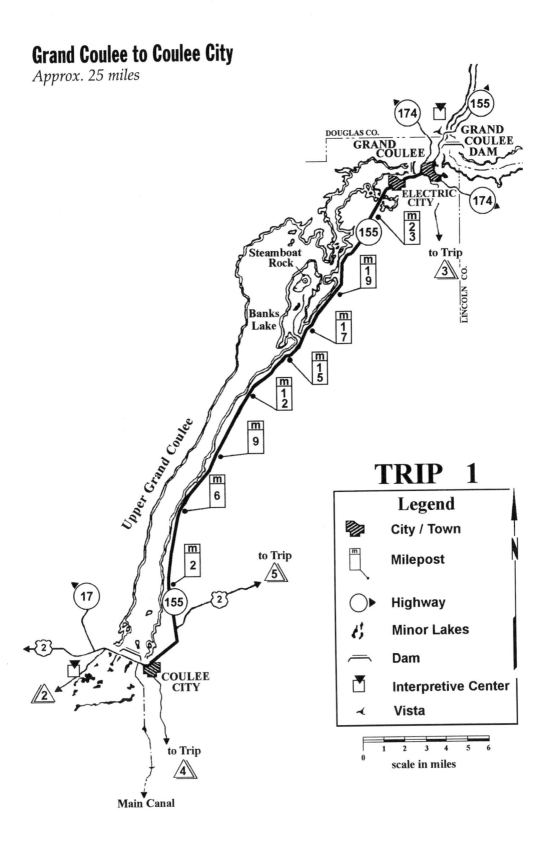

Grand Coulee to Coulee City

State Highway 155 to U.S. Highway 2

LENGTH: 25 MILES ONE WAY, MILEPOSTS: 1–25

MILEPOST 15

Along the highway from the city of Grand Coulee south to Steamboat Rock State Park (N MP 15 = north milepost 15) stand huge masses of light gray granite rocks. These exposures represent the oldest rocks left in Grant County. The rocks began their existence as sediments in shallow seas hundreds of millions of years ago. Over time, these sediments were buried under hundreds of feet of earth and compacted. Around 65 million years ago, the sediments were transformed through intense heat and pressure to form the granite, gneiss, and schist rocks present here today. Following the transformation of sediments to light colored crystalline rocks, the old seabed was uplifted and eroded. The remaining rocks are exposed as mountainous terrain typical of the area today and similar to the relief further north in Okanogan County.

The geology in Grant County is missing millions of years from the stratigraphic record between the formation of just-mentioned granite rocks and much more recently erupted basalt lavas. This time is not represented in the stratigraphic record because the land likely was continually being uplifted and eroded. What happened to erase the time or prevent it from accumulating in the geologic record remains a mystery.

Granitic outcrops between Steamboat Rock and Grand Coule

Catastrophic flooding scooped out the Grand Coulee channel. The flooding swept away basalt rock and sediments and gouged out the area more than 13,000 years ago. The Grand Coulee was formed when floodwaters forced the Columbia River to run south because the Okanogan ice lobe of the continental glacier dammed the gorge about where Grand Coulee Dam now stands. The floodwaters created a series of interconnected rocky canyons, channels, and coulees called scablands. The Grand Coulee scablands run from the Columbia River at Grand Coulee Dam to just north of the city of Soap Lake and vary in width from 1 to 14 miles.

The Missoula Floods are so named because they originated in Montana before charging west through Idaho and central Washington state. The floods carried an estimated 500 cubic miles of glacial meltwater that originated from a lake that was up to 2,000 feet deep, 800 miles long, and covered 3,000 square miles. Turn back to DIAGRAM 3 on page 10 in the general geology introduction to visualize the extent of the floods shown as a graphic illustration with Grant County superimposed on the area affected by flooding.

A significant portion of the floodwaters from Lake Missoula surged over and through Glacial Lake Columbia, a large Columbia River lake that stretched between Grand Coulee east to the Spokane River. The combined flood volume sent a torrent of water charging down the Grand Coulee.

MILEPOST 25

As the floodwaters scoured out the bottom of the channel at North Dam just north of Electric City, the basalt flows higher up on the hill lost their base and slid down into the coulee. A profile of the geology at the north abutment of North Dam (DIAGRAM 4—PRE-FLOOD AND POST-FLOOD STRATIGRAPHY AT NORTH DAM, page 19) illustrates the severity of the shifting basalt, called a slide block, which rotated and tilted to a forty-five degree angle. Bore holes drilled at the dam site uncovered a buried cobble-filled channel confirming the presence of the flood that caused the slides. To reach this location, turn into the North Dam Rest Area (N MP 25). Note the tilted lava flows across Banks Lake where the slide forms the north abutment of the dam.

MILEPOSTS 22–23

South of Electric City, the highway cuts into the Nespelem Formation, a lake-deposited stratified silt and clay formation. These deposits show a series of finely layered annual beds or varves. The varves represent the yearly accumulation of fine-grained sediments from a glacier-fed lake that occupied the coulee floor after the ancient catastrophic floods passed through it. The fine-textured lake deposits are easily seen in road cuts between Electric City and Grand Coulee (S MP 22–23) and in other isolated locations along the edges of the lakes in the Grand Coulee.

The upper Grand Coulee canyon follows a structure in the basalt lava

DIAGRAM 4—Pre-Flood and Post-Flood Stratigraphy at North Dam

Basalt at North Dam Site Before Slide Event

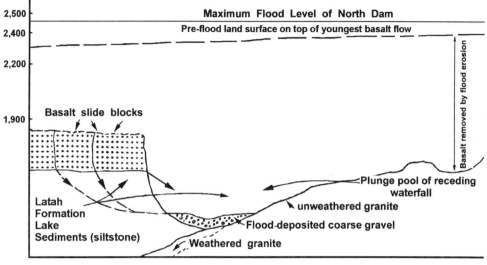

North Dam Profile
After flood erosion released Lake Columbia
and before north wall slid into channel

Basalt at North Dam Site After Slide Event

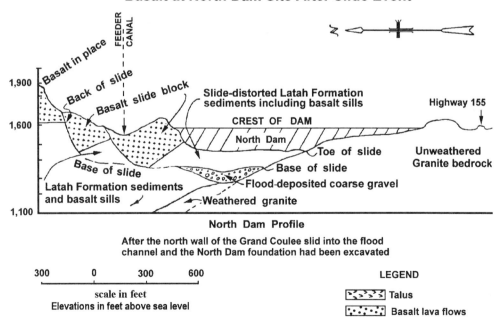

North Dam Profile
After the north wall of the Grand Coulee slid into the flood
channel and the North Dam foundation had been excavated

scale in feet
Elevations in feet above sea level

LEGEND

Talus

Basalt lava flows

Steamboat Rock looking north

formation that dips to the southeast. At Electric City, the Grand Coulee heads south along the fractured basalt lava flows of a structure known as the Barker Monocline.

MILEPOST 17

Basalt which now laps onto the granitic rock north of Steamboat Rock (N MP 17) is the northern edge of widespread "lava lakes" that filled low-lying basins in south central Washington beginning nearly 30 million years ago. The basalt flowed like warm molasses from cracks, fissures or dikes oozing out over the land surface repeatedly over millions of years. Successive outpourings of lava continued to cover the old landscape layer by layer by extending to higher lands beyond the perimeter of older flows. This process continued repeatedly from 6 to 17 million years ago. In some places, there are up to 10,000 feet of basalt lavas.

Lava flows are stacked one on another all along the Grand Coulee and may be seen in the nearly vertical walls exposed along Banks Lake and Steamboat Rock. All flows cool and tend to fracture into three distinct zones. Flow characteristics typical of each flow are easy to see all along this route. A porous-looking or vesicular crust at the top of each flow is caused by gases escaping to the surface of the molten lava and is similar to the effect created in a freshly opened pop bottle. The vesicular crust cooled and solidified very quickly. The vesicular surface is underlain by blocky structures known as the entablature and massive vertical columns called the colonnade that cooled much more slowly (illustrated in DIA-GRAM 2—PROFILE THROUGH A BASALT LAVA FLOW on page 3).

MILEPOST 15

Steamboat Rock, so named because in profile it looks like a giant steamboat, is actually a basalt mesa (N MP 15) that resisted stripping by glacial meltwaters that cascaded over it. This came about as the horseshoe-shaped waterfall excavating the Grand Coulee split in two, reunited, broke through into the Columbia Valley, and drained Glacial Lake Columbia.

Notice that a basalt slide block is tilted and slumped against the north end of Steamboat Rock.

Each year seasonal surface runoff and perennial springs cascade from "hanging valleys" on the east and west walls of the Grand Coulee.

Granitic rock fragments on top of Steamboat Rock were not native to this location. These boulders on top of the rock, along with thick accumulations of sand and gravel around the base of Steamboat Rock, characterize the extreme range of particle sizes dropped by floodwaters. South of Steamboat Rock, the only granite present is flood derived. The granitic rocks, known as erratics, were carried in on glacial ice or rolled along the bed of the flood channel by high velocity flood flows.

MILEPOSTS 9–19

The record of flood erosion and deposition near Steamboat Rock lies exposed as sandy or gravelly bars and cut banks. Across the road from the Steamboat Rock Boat Launch (S MP 19) at the mouth of Northrup Canyon, cross-bedded, unsorted sand and gravel layers many feet thick are shown within the vertical cuts in the gravel pit. Immediately south of Steamboat Rock west of the highway, look for gravel bar and lake deposits dumped on the inside of a channel curve in water that slowed and redirected its flow in the coulee (S MP 9). Large granite and basalt boulders were haphazardly thrown onto the surface at this location. Note the wide range of sediment sizes in this small localized area (MP 9–10).

South of Steamboat Rock high up on the east rock wall of the coulee is a rare example of one of the fissures or vertical cracks called dikes that allowed molten lava to rise from its deep earth source (E MP 12). Although basalt lava flows with vesicular surface structures and vertical cooling cracks or columns are typical, the internal flow characteristics here are really atypical. The dike has a non-vesicular upper layer, indicative of a lava flow that did not rise to the surface, and horizontal columns may be seen in this basalt dike which cut between or through several lava flows. The horizontal layer above the dike, which forced its way between the lava flows, is called a sill (illustrated in DIAGRAM 5—BASALT LAVA DIKE AND SILL, page 23). In this case, the lava sill intrusion did not reach the surface, so it, too, has atypical flow features. Look west across the coulee for a sight of the same sill exposed in the face of the basalt wall above the west shore of Banks Lake.

MILEPOSTS 6–7

Flow upon flow of lava is exposed in the vertical basalt walls that rise as high as 900 feet in the Grand Coulee. All along the Grand Coulee excellent views show off basalt flow characteristics. State Highway 155 (between MP 6–7) cuts through several flows displaying more typical basalt flow characteristics; e.g., with holey or vesicular surface structure, blocky structure, and vertical columns. This stretch of road is known locally as the "Million Dollar Mile". It cost more than $1 million to excavate the basalt and construct the road in the process of rerouting State Highway 155 from its original location along the coulee floor to its present location to prevent it from being flooded when Banks Lake was filled in 1951.

In the Grand Coulee the basalt rock walls and slopes covered with loose angular rocks, known as talus, show the result of thousands of years of freezing and thawing since the catastrophic floodwaters receded. The accumulation of rain water and snow melt in cracks and crevices forced rock fragments to fall from the cliffs as it froze and thawed and continues to this day.

Natural refrigerators occur along the base of talus slopes where accumulated moisture is frozen during the winter. The cold temperature under the broken rock results in a drainage of cool air emerging from the toe of the talus slope through the summer months. Places where the rocks have been removed from the toe of a large north-facing talus slope are good places to store food. Pioneers called these places "ice caves." Though they are nice places to have a lunch break on a hot day, please be careful since rattlesnakes like them too.

Look for numerous hanging valleys where ancient streams older than the coulee were cut off by floodwaters leaving channels suspended high up on the coulee walls. The water emerging from these stream valleys occasionally empties its load on the edge of the Grand Coulee and drains into the scabland below. Grass, shrubs, and trees on the sheer coulee rock walls indicate the emergence of ground water as it seeps out of seams between basalt layers. Spectacular waterfalls can be observed on occasions when snow melt or other water plunges out of the hanging valleys onto

Diagram 5—Basalt Lava Dike and Sill

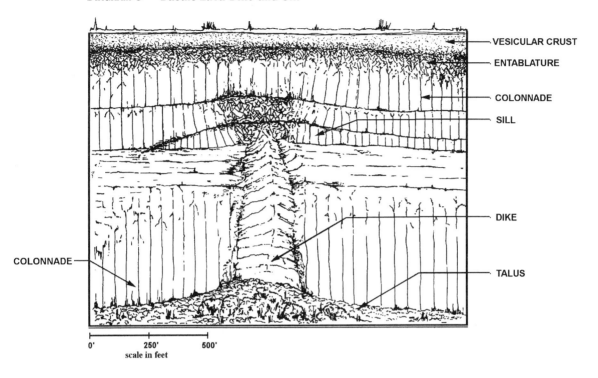

VESICULAR CRUST
ENTABLATURE
COLONNADE
SILL
DIKE
TALUS
COLONNADE

0'   250'   500'
scale in feet

the talus deposits below the cliffs. In the winter, the water leaving these seeps and stream valleys freezes, creating fascinating ice sculptures.

MILEPOST 2

An exposure of tilted lava flow may be seen along the highway (E MP 2) north of Coulee City. Here, the Coulee Monocline is the result of deep-seated faulting and settling of the basalt lava flows in response to the thousands of feet of lava that erupted onto the earth's crust from the earth's interior. These changes are visualized if one imagines what would happen to a stack of hotcakes lying on top of two overlapping pieces of a broken plate—warped, tilted, and buckled surfaces.

The lower Grand Coulee follows the Coulee Monocline which turns east about four miles north of Coulee City. Here it abruptly drops 1,000 feet, creating the base level from which the Coulee's receding waterfall was initiated. At this point the lava flows dip south to form the surface of the Dry Falls basin.

Banks Lake to Soap Lake
Approx. 20 miles

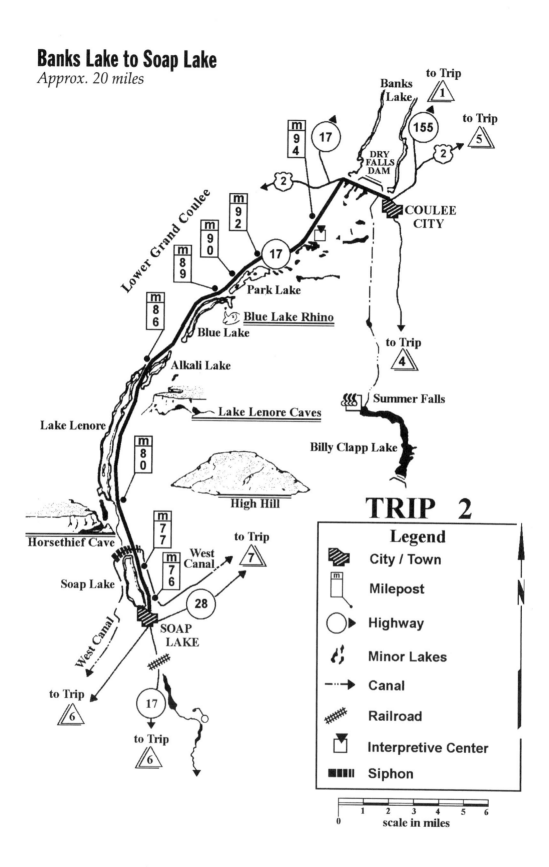

TRIP 2

Legend

City / Town
Milepost
Highway
Minor Lakes
Canal
Railroad
Interpretive Center
Siphon

scale in miles
0 1 2 3 4 5 6

Banks Lake to Soap Lake

State Highway 17

LENGTH: 20 MILES ONE WAY, MILEPOSTS: 76–96

Begin at the intersection of U. S. Highway 2 and State Highway 17 at the west end of Dry Falls Dam.

MILEPOST 94

At the Dry Falls Interpretive Center Overlook on State Highway 17 (N MP 94), magnificent views of an ancient waterfall site and excellent profiles of many lava flows piled on top of each other grace the panoramic scene. Dry Falls is the site of a 14,000-year-old waterfall 350 feet high by 3.5 miles wide. It is estimated that the water coming across the top of the falls may have been as much as 300 feet deep above the top of the falls. When the enormous waterfall or cataract was a raging river of glacial floodwater, gigantic icebergs, mud, sand, gravel, and huge boulders cascaded over it. The resulting waterfall was five times the width of Niagara Falls. Today it has created the breathtaking views, numerous plunge pools, and beautiful lakes from Dry Falls Lake south to Soap Lake. When water was cascading over the Dry Falls cataracts, floodwaters would have stretched across 14 miles of scabland channels to the east of the Interpretive Center. "Battleship Rock" is an island of rock that separates the lakes below the Dry Falls Interpretive Center. This rock feature resisted flood erosion and is an isolated mesa similar to Steamboat

Dry Falls Panorama

Rock near the north end of Banks Lake. Seven horseshoe-shaped cataracts in a row may be seen looking across the Dry Falls complex.

MILEPOST 92

Notice that the floods peeled off portions of lava flows and left steep-sided mesas. The velocity and volume of the massive water flow were so large that it stripped out large areas of less resistant lava flows and randomly plucked, gouged, and sculpted the topography as we see it today. The huge floods that swept through the coulee lasted a mere two weeks. An outing through Sun Lakes State Park (N MP 92) is a good chance to view close up some of these water-carved features. The road east from the park to Deep Lake provides an opportunity to observe other cataract features formed simultaneously with the Dry Falls erosion.

Lower Grand Coulee looking south from the curve above Park Lake

From Park Lake to Soap Lake, the floodwaters excavated the greatly fractured and tilted basalt rock of the Coulee Monocline. Initial floodwater erosion started as a waterfall near the south end of Lake Lenore which progressed upstream to Dry Falls when the flooding ended. At the same time, another waterfall began north of the city of Soap Lake and worked its way through the coulee until it established a new base level for waterfalls at Lake Lenore. The same flood events scoured a gap between High Hill and Pinto Ridge four miles east of Lake Lenore and a gap on the east end of Pinto Ridge ten miles east of Lake Lenore. The west wall of the coulee between Soap Lake and Park Lake contains the same series of lava flows exposed on the east coulee wall at Park Lake at a much lower elevation. This is the result of vertical displacement of the rock strata during the time between the lava extrusion (Miocene) and the Ice Age floods (Pleistocene).

MILEPOSTS 85–92

Observe the tilted lava flows on the north edge of the road by the Blue Lake Resort (MP 90). Visualize the angle of tilt by standing underneath the rock face by the edge of the road. Outcrops of tilted basalt islands are present in Lake Lenore and along the highway north to Park Lake at Coulee Lodge Resort opposite Park Lake Road (MP 85–90). DIAGRAM 6—GEOLOGIC CROSS-SECTION, GRAND COULEE AT PARK LAKE LOOKING NORTH on page 28 shows where to find these features (MP 92). North where the highway climbs out of the coulee the east-dipping lava flows of the Coulee Monocline diverted waters and exposed the fractured rock of the lower Grand Coulee to the flood erosion.

Lava flows erupted and oozed out intermittently over a period that lasted 11 million years. Between lava eruptions sedimentation, weathering, and erosion took place. Petrified trees are preserved in layers of these sediments deposited between basalt flows throughout Grant County. One such place is on the the east shore of Blue Lake where fossilized logs are preserved and embedded. More than 100 species of trees, shrubs and other plants have been identified from fossil leaves and wood found in the interflow sediments from this part of Washington. Many fine examples of the trees are on display at the Ginkgo State Park Headquarters at Vantage.

Embedded in the basalt along the east edge of Blue Lake is a rare fossil impression of an early rhinoceros. The rhinoceros apparently died in a pond and was engulfed by advancing lava. It is preserved as a whole body cast in the basalt rock. A three-dimensional diorama at the Dry Falls Interpretive Center (N MP 94) recreates how the rhinoceros may have been engulfed by the molten lava and explains how it was preserved. The rhino cast is accessible by boat but since it is on private property, landowner permission should be obtained before proceeding up the steep cliff. Care should also be taken when scrambling up over talus and climbing up onto the rock ledges as the rock is steep and footing is precarious. Also, remember this is rattlesnake country; try to avoid running and keep your eyes open.

Wherever the hot lava flows entered water, the rapid cooling created "pillows" or rounded masses of basalt. Pillow basalts are exposed in the roadcut (MP 89) on the west side of the road.

Coarse-textured soil and rock rolled along at the bottom of any flood

Diagram 6—Geologic Cross-Section, Grand Coulee at Park Lake looking North

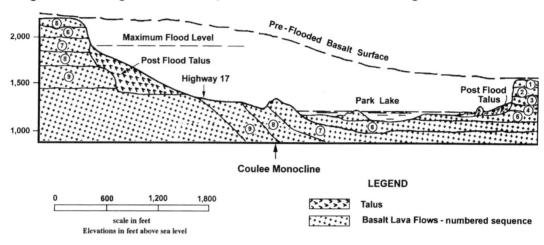

0   600   1,200   1,800

scale in feet

Elevations in feet above sea level

LEGEND

Talus

Basalt Lava Flows - numbered sequence

stream is referred to as bed load. Bed load deposits of the Missoula Flood were stranded locally as huge bars along the east edges of Park Lake, Blue Lake, and the south end of Lake Lenore.

Closed depressions left by flood erosion remained full of water forming lakes which persisted for long periods. Eventually, the climate became as dry as it is today. Most lakes dried up except in the deepest depressions where water levels are sustained by ground water springs.

Varves or thinly bedded layers that represent yearly accumulations of fine-textured lake sediments may be seen in the roadcut on State Highway 17 north and south of the Blue Lake Rest Area (N & S MP 89–90). These deposits indicate this was a stable water body into which volcanic ash and soil were blown or washed thousands of years ago. Many of these deposits originated from areas to the north covered by melting glaciers. Finely ground soil and rock pulverized by glacial action is known as rock flour and was released from the glacial ice as it melted and settled out in large lakes.

Imagine the area from Dry Falls to the Burlington Northern Railroad just south of Soap Lake, a distance of about 19 miles, covered by a huge lake. This once-continuous lake must have been an important feature for the early Native American inhabitants of the region.

The lakes between Dry Falls Lake and Soap Lake contain water whose only source seeps out of the surrounding rock formations and whose only natural outlet is by evaporation. Before the Columbia Basin Irrigation Project diverted water from the Columbia River through this area, the outlet from Blue Lake and Alkali Lake dried up in the summer.

28

The outlets between the lakes run continuously throughout the year now augmented by waters carried through the Columbia Basin Project facilities, which seeps through the lava bedrock.

The formation of a series of rock shelters or caves above Lake Lenore occurred as floodwaters ripped apart less resistant contacts between basalt flows. Plunge pools, basins and potholes were created and the rock was removed by powerful whirlpools. After the floods receded, freezing and thawing occurred and accumulations of talus and rock-fall nearly closed off the undercut areas that form the Lake Lenore Caves (S MP 85). These natural rock shelters were used as overnight camps and cache or storage sites by early nomadic hunters and gatherers thousands of years ago. The caves are well marked and easily reached by a short trail from a graveled parking lot. Other rock shelters are perched along the cliff walls along many of the lakes in the Grand Coulee. One of the deepest is "Horsethief Cave," a cave big enough to hide many horses stolen from local ranches over the years.

MILEPOST 80

On the south end of Lake Lenore, dipping lava flows on the south (S MP 80) side of High Hill can be seen on the east side of the coulee. The initial flood of water down this dipping slope initiated the waterfall that cut its way upstream to the present Dry Falls site. Pumps on Lake Lenore

Lake Lenore Caves

now carry water out of the coulee into a nearby irrigation canal that waters the Columbia Basin Irrigation Project. The pumps are designed to prevent the lakes from rising above their natural lake surfaces. Pumping started in 1951 and by 1959 the alkalinity of Lake Lenore had freshened enough to support alkali-resistant Lahontan cutthroat trout fish populations introduced in 1979.

The West Canal of the Columbia Basin Irrigation Project crosses the Grand Coulee just north of Soap Lake in a huge 2.5-mile-long steel-lined concrete pipe. This pipe conveys the entire flow of the West Canal and drops it into another open canal section along the hillside that eventually winds past Ephrata. The water pumped from Lake Lenore is pumped by a relift into the Soap Lake Siphon.

Here it is appropriate to explain how a complex of irrigation water canals are superimposed on the landscape. Irrigation water is diverted from Grand Coulee Dam and runs through the Feeder Canal into Banks Lake. From the south end of Banks Lake, the water travels down the Main Canal through two 10,000-foot-long tunnels taking a 165-foot drop into Billy Clapp Lake via Summer Falls. South of Summer Falls and Billy Clapp Lake, a distribution system known as the Bifurcation Works divides the water into the West Canal and the East Low Canal. The West Canal delivers irrigation water to the western half of the Columbia Basin and then through the Frenchman Hills onto the Royal Slope. It passes near or around the cities of Soap Lake, Ephrata, Quincy, and George. The East Low Canal passes 4 miles east of Moses Lake, bends around Warden, passes 6 miles east of Othello and outlets into Scooteney Reservoir east of the Saddle Mountains. More than 670,000 acres are irrigated from this particular diversion of irrigation water from the Columbia River.

MILEPOST 78

The walls of the Grand Coulee north of Soap Lake (N MP 78) display classic examples of columnar basalt. The uppermost flow surfaces are deeply weathered, indicating a history of lengthy exposure to the forces of nature. Notice that the uppermost flows on the west side of the coulee are capped with a final layer of fine-grained light colored sediments called the Ringold Formation which accumulated in the bed of a lake that once filled this basin. This one small isolated exposure reveals the whole geologic history of the area between the end of the lava eruptions and the great Lake Missoula flood.

Soap Lake (MP 76), the last lake in the chain of Grand Coulee lakes, lies in a small deeply eroded topographic basin in the basalt bedrock. The lake gets its name because the waters foam like a bubble bath, especially on windy days, and the water has a soapy, slippery feel. This is because of the high concentration of sodium carbonate salts in the water. There are other minerals in the water as well, including lithium, copper, tungsten, titanium, vanadium, and iron. The bottom of Soap Lake is partially filled with cobbles and very coarse gravel blanketed with a thick bed of clay. Soap Lake is in a closed basin without an outlet. Evaporation concentrates the natural alkalinity of the ground water that flows into the lake. Acidity or alkalinity is expressed as a numeral with a pH reading of 7 considered neutral. Soap Lake has a pH reading of 9. The salt content or alkalinity is so high that no fish survive in it. A close look at the Soap Lake shoreline may reveal a small crustacean called "brine shrimp" typically found in many of the saline lakes in the western states.

Though no one comes to fish, Soap Lake has been a major attraction for hundreds of years. People from all over the world have been drawn to Soap Lake's water, famous for its curative powers. Native Americans called the lake "Smokiam," which means healing waters. Before the turn of the nineteenth century Soap Lake was known as Sanitarium Lake. The Soap Lake Hospital was built after World War I as a veterans hospital for the treatment of Buerger's Disease, a painful circulatory disease triggered by a hypersensitivity to nicotine. The Soap Lake water seems to have relieved sufferers of some of the symptoms. Since then, the National Psoriasis Foundation has endorsed the lake water as unique for helping some people relieve symptoms of that condition. Many of the town's residents have double plumbing so that lake water is pumped into their homes. Although the heyday of Soap Lake water as a medicinal cure-all is long past, people who believe in the lake's therapeutic value still flock to the lake to bathe in its foaming waters and use the mud as a poultice.

With the development of the Columbia Basin Irrigation Project in the early 1950s, Soap Lake was threatened with the loss of its unique alkaline character when increasing amounts of fresh water began seeping into it. Seven ground water interception wells were consequently drilled into the gravels underlying the clay bed beneath the lake. The wells around the perimeter of the lake were designed to keep this fresh ground water from rising to dilute the saline lake water.

Soap Lake water contains two types of salts: calcium carbonates and sodium carbonates. Some of the salts have remained in solution while some carbonates have precipitated out. As long as the interception pumps continue to operate, the salty or alkaline nature of Soap Lake will be maintained.

At Soap Lake (MP 76), a high-rise fractured basalt hill called the Soap Lake anticline (S MP 77) dips gently to the north and then more steeply to the south. Basalt lava flows, which were laid down layer upon layer, became warped and buckled by underlying crustal adjustments. Over time, the land surface reflected the warped structure of the underlying basement rock. This phenomenon can be observed where the lower Grand Coulee, along the east edge of Soap Lake on State Highway 17, cuts through the arch or anticline, which extends and rises up eastward. The floodwater gouged the fractured basalt rocks at the crest of the anticline where the highway now passes along the east edge of Soap Lake. Since these surfaces were buckled and heavily fractured they were easy to dislodge by water and often provided the source rock plucked in the course of floodwater action. As the water surged out of the mouth of the Grand Coulee onto the broad plain south of Soap Lake, it slowed and abruptly dropped its large rock passengers out across an area that extends more than 10 miles. The entire surface of the area from Dry Falls to Soap Lake virtually uncoupled the joint structure of the basalt that was plucked apart by the mighty force of the floodwater driving into it.

Tilted lava flows at Alkali Lake

Crown Point Vista to Grand Coulee to Hartline
Approx. 24 miles

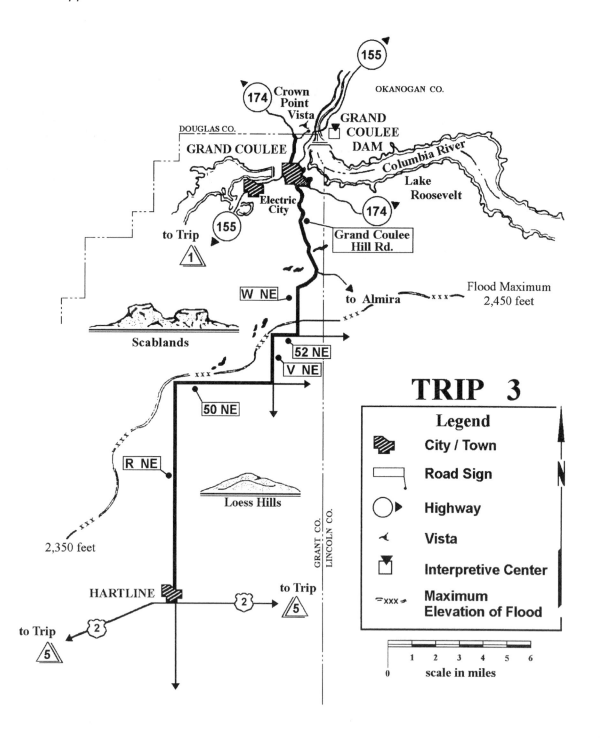

Crown Point Vista to Grand Coulee to Hartline

State Highway 174, Grand Coulee Hill Road, and County roads R NE, V NE, 50 NE, and 52 NE

LENGTH: 24 MILES, MILEPOSTS: 19–22

Take State Highway 174 and then south and west on Grand Coulee Hill Road to Hartline. Unfortunately there are no milepost markers south of Grand Coulee on the Grand Coulee Hill Road to Hartline on this route. However, roads are well marked in accordance with the county road grid at one-mile intervals.

MILEPOST 22

To reach Crown Point Vista, take State Highway 174 north from Grand Coulee about 2.7 miles to Crown Point Vista Road (N MP 22). Turn right onto the Crown Point Vista Road. While driving toward the vista, look at the roadcut on the north side of the road to see semi-consolidated glacial tills. Tills are unsorted non-stratified sediment carried within glacial ice and dropped on this northern edge of the county when the ice melted. Look across the Columbia River from the vista shelter to a large gravel pit used to provide aggregate for the concrete in the Grand Coulee Dam.

Downstream from Grand Coulee Dam is the Grand Coulee Dam Visitor Center. The Visitor Center is a good place to view the magnificence of the dam and explore the history of its development. During the summer, be sure to set time aside for the evening Laser Light show at the Dam Visitor Center. The show uses the cascading water on the face of the dam as a three-dimensional screen. On the return to Grand Coulee notice an electrical switch yard where power from the dam's generators is transformed for distribution over the cross-country power lines.

For a picturesque view of Grand Coulee Dam and Lake Roosevelt, the lake formed in the Columbia River valley behind the Grand Coulee Dam, return to the town of Grand Coulee and proceed east on State Highway 174. Turn right on the Grand Coulee Hill Road that winds up the hill to the south.

After taking in the view, continue on the Grand Coulee Hill Road past channeled scablands that were carved out and plucked clean by floodwater.

The flow of water that scoured this scabland eventually entered the upper Grand Coulee by way of Northrup Creek (east of Steamboat Rock). The scabland topography of very shallow soils, numerous depressions, potholes, basalt rock outcrops, and closed wet basins characterize the hummocky irregular relief of this area.

After 6 miles the road forks. The left fork leads to Almira. Bear right (southwest) toward Hartline. Turn right (west) onto road 52 NE to its intersection with road V NE. It is interesting to visualize that at this corner the maximum flood level is estimated to have been about thirty feet deep. The wall of water engulfing the entire Grand Coulee channel would have been close to 900 feet deep. Soils to the north and west of here are scoured by the flood and are less than one foot deep from bedrock. To the east and south, the land was spared from the flood and soils are over five feet deep contrasting with shallow scabland soils to the northwest. The upper limits of flood erosion can be tracked for miles as windblown silts, called loess, dominate the landscape all the way to the town of Hartline.

After turning onto road V NE, travel south and drive 2 miles to the intersection of 50 NE. Turn right on road 50 NE and drive west 4 miles turning left onto road R NE. The maximum flood level reached this corner. Steamboat Rock lies to the northwest and the width of the Grand Coulee flood channel is about 4 miles at this point. It narrows down to 2 miles wide between here and the site of the receding waterfall south of Steamboat Rock that plunged 700 feet.

Nine miles to the north, the Okanogan lobe of the glacier forced the flood to divert its floodwater southward down the Grand Coulee and Moses Coulee.

As road R NE descends toward Hartline, look for white patches of rock exposed in summer fallowed fields which are subsoils cemented into lime rock called caliche. The caliche condition is characteristic of subsoils in semi-arid climates where evapotranspiration potential exceeds annual rainfall.

The valleys carry intermittent streams only during the winter, spring, and/or summer when melting snow or rain runs off or during infrequent cloudbursts; then water flows west to plunge over the cliffs into the Grand Coulee.

Drive south on R NE to Hartline at the intersection of R NE and U. S. Highway 2.

The Grand Coulee Hill Road winds its way through shallow rocky scablands and rolling deep loess-covered hills to Hartline. View is looking north at intersection of Road 47 NE and V NE.

Coulee City to Stratford
Approx. 15 miles

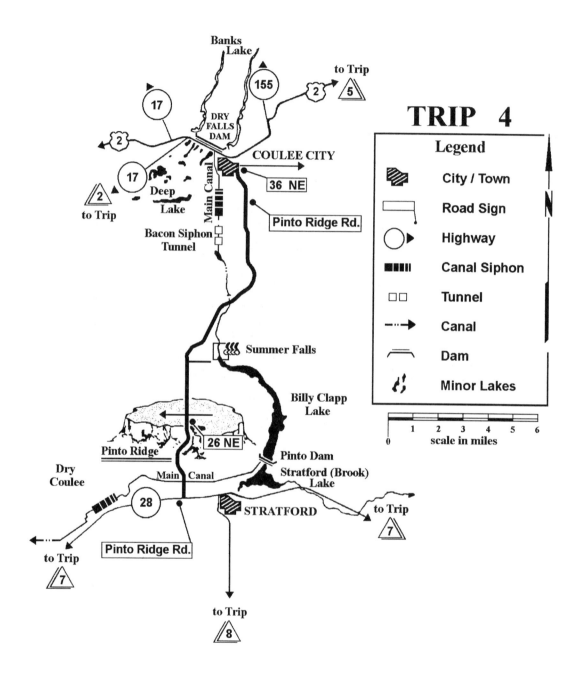

Banks Lake

▲
155

to Trip
2 △5

17

DRY FALLS DAM

2

COULEE CITY

17

36 NE

△2
to Trip ▲

Deep Lake

Main Canal

Pinto Ridge Rd.

Bacon Siphon Tunnel

TRIP 4

Legend

⬙	City / Town
▭	Road Sign
◯▶	Highway
▪▪▪▪▪	Canal Siphon
▢▢	Tunnel
—··▶	Canal
⌒	Dam
♪	Minor Lakes

scale in miles
0 1 2 3 4 5 6

N

≋ Summer Falls

Billy Clapp Lake

Pinto Ridge

26 NE

Pinto Dam
Stratford (Brook) Lake

Dry Coulee

Main Canal

28

STRATFORD

to Trip
△7

Pinto Ridge Rd.

◀—··
to Trip
△7

to Trip
△8

Coulee City to Stratford

U. S. Highway 2 south to State Highway 28 via Pinto Ridge Road

LENGTH: 15 MILES ONE WAY

Be sure to check your odometer from the outskirts of Coulee City because there are no milepost signs along this route.

On the south end of Banks Lake is Dry Falls Dam, known locally as South Dam, which was completed on November 6, 1949. Dry Falls Dam is an earth-fill dam that impounds the water at the south end of Banks Lake.

Banks Lake is the Columbia Basin Irrigation Project's "water tank" providing irrigation water to more than 670,000 acres. Approximately two to three percent of the Columbia River is permitted to be pumped into Banks Lake. The lake is contained by earth fill dams at both ends because the coulee bottom is slightly higher at the south outlet end than at the north inlet end. In addition, the coulee floor was eroded deeper within the confines of the walled coulee.

The power plant at the dam uses the drop from Banks Lake to gravity feed the water into the Main Canal. Seepage water escaping from Banks Lake and water seeping from the Main Canal augments natural ground water flowing into lakes south of Dry Falls Dam.

The town of Coulee City draws its water from a series of naturally occurring springs referred to locally as the McIntee Springs. These springs percolate through flood-deposited sand and gravel. Historically, Coulee City began its existence more than 100 years ago as a stagecoach stop with the only potable water between Spokane and Wenatchee. These ancient springs continue to discharge ground water from the Hartline Basin. Other springs along the route of the Burlington Northern Railroad to the south occur at Wilson Creek and at Beezley Springs (Ephrata) were not on the direct route operated by the stagecoach.

Turn into Coulee City across U. S. Highway 2 from the Coulee City Park. Drive south and east through Coulee City to find the Pinto Ridge Road.

Southeast of Coulee City on the Pinto Ridge Road, drive through the scoured basalt scablands. About 1 mile southwest of Coulee City, stop or slow down for a glimpse of Deep Lake off to the west. Deep Lake lies in a flood-scoured plunge pool east of Dry Falls.

Four miles south of Coulee City is an excellent example of pillow basalts exposed in a roadcut. Pillow basalts occur where molten lava flowed into a body of water. Here at this location, the contact of the lava with water created pillows or rounded nodules. The existence of pillow basalts, petrified wood, or other fossils all show that the lava flows advanced across ponds, lakes, streams, and forests. The advance of the lava into water also caused chemical reactions and allowed a commingling of molten magma with sedimentary diatomaceous earth deposits at this location. The resulting material is called nontronite, a deposit that has a high clay content that permeated the pillow basalt layer. These deposits have orange or red hues with much brighter and lighter colors than the dark crystalline rocks around them.

After crossing the Main Canal about 7 miles south of Coulee City, caliche-capped finely layered lake deposits of the Ringold Formation can be seen above the west side of the road. Here the floods deposited sand and gravel bed load over the top of the lake bed deposits leaving the caliche deposits intact under the flood-deposited sand and gravel.

Look to the south and east for a flood-cut channel around the east end of Pinto Ridge. Now occupying this channel is Billy Clapp Lake (also called Long Lake) impounded by Pinto Dam. Toward the west the Dry Coulee canyon scabland separates Pinto Ridge from High Hill.

About 8 miles north of Stratford or 9 miles south of Coulee City, turn east to Summer Falls and drive down the hill where the road follows a narrow valley to Summer Falls State Park. The steep hillside on the south is the front of a basalt fault block that was thrust from the north toe of Pinto Ridge. Basalt on the north side of the road is part of flat-lying lava flows at the base of Pinto Ridge. The valley to Summer Falls was excavated by floodwaters plunging into the highly fractured front of the fault block. Summer Falls runs only during the irrigation season, March through mid-October, charged by irrigation water diverted through Banks Lake from the Columbia River at Grand Coulee Dam.

Back on the Pinto Ridge Road about 9.5 miles south of Coulee City, drive south to climb the north slope of Pinto Ridge. A sand bar, exposed in roadcuts on both sides of the road, was dropped by the floods. Broad expanses of rock covered with little or no soil is evidence of the flood's scouring power.

A sudden increase in soil depth defines the maximum limit of floodwater erosion in the area between Pinto Ridge and Dry Falls. Ten miles south of Coulee City or north of road 26 NE, soils are deeper than 60 inches to bedrock and consist of windblown silts called loess. The uneroded loess landscape to the south was not disturbed or removed by the floods. By looking at this area, imagine what the area would have looked like before the ravages of the floods stripped off a million-year-old surface and gouged out the coulees and scablands. Before the floods, this whole area could have resembled the Palouse region of southeastern Washington underlain by tens of feet of loess which thickens from west to east.

About 14 miles south of Coulee City, cross the Main Canal. A side trip east on the graveled canal road takes the traveler to Pinto Dam, a compacted earth-fill dam that impounds the water in Billy Clapp Lake. Floodwater flowing down Crab Creek from the Cheney-Palouse scablands to the east scooped out Stratford Lake, Round Lake, Rocky Coulee, Black Rock Coulee, and enlarged the pre-existing valley of Crab Creek on its way south to Moses Lake. At Moses Lake, floodwaters from the Grand Coulee merged with floodwaters from Crab Creek to fill the area between Quincy and Moses Lake.

Summer Falls, off Pinto Ridge Road, runs only part of the year.

Coulee City to the Grant-Lincoln County Line

Approx. 17 miles

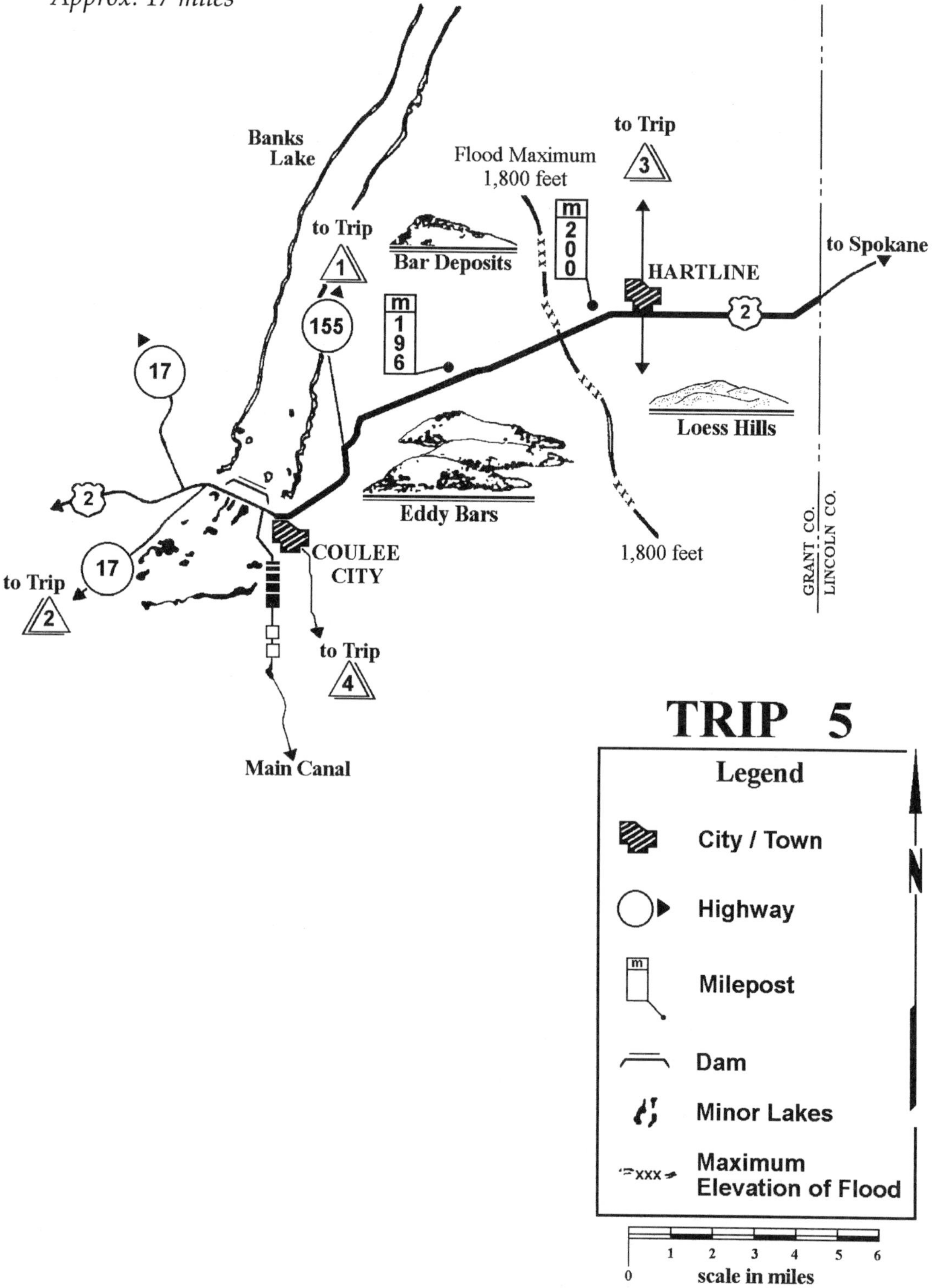

Banks Lake

Flood Maximum
1,800 feet

to Trip
△3

to Trip
△1

to Spokane

Bar Deposits

HARTLINE

〔2〕

155

Loess Hills

17

1,800 feet

2

17

COULEE
CITY

Eddy Bars

GRANT CO.
LINCOLN CO.

to Trip
△2

to Trip
△4

Main Canal

TRIP 5

Legend

City / Town

Highway

Milepost

Dam

Minor Lakes

xxx Maximum
Elevation of Flood

N

1 2 3 4 5 6

0   scale in miles

Coulee City to the Grant-Lincoln County Line

U. S. Highway 2

LENGTH: 17 MILES ONE WAY, MILEPOSTS: 191–208

Proceed on U. S. Highway 2 from Coulee City east to the county line.

MILEPOST 194

The hills east of Coulee City (MP 194) are the eastern flank of flood-deposited sand and gravel bars. A portion of the central mass of the bar west of Coulee City was removed by the last great flood.

MILEPOST 196

Floodwaters spread eastward into the Hartline basin from the main Grand Coulee channel and deposited "giant bars" in the slack water of the Hartline Basin east of Coulee City. The gravel and sand pit (MP 196) shows the sandy nature of these bar deposits. Farther south floodwaters eroded adjacent uplands and gouged out coulees.

MILEPOST 198

To the east (MP 198) on high ground, loess covered hills stood unaffected by the floods. Maximum flood surface elevation at Grand Coulee was 2,450 feet. Anything above this elevation was not touched by the floods. At Coulee City, the maximum flood elevation was 1,800 feet. In the area between Moses Lake and Quincy, the critical elevation was 1,355 feet and in the lower Crab Creek near Othello and Pasco areas the high point floodwaters reached the 1,200-foot elevation point. Compare this with a Banks Lake elevation of 1,570 feet and a Royal City elevation of 1,050 feet.

Soap Lake to Moses Lake to Ephrata

Approx. 32 miles

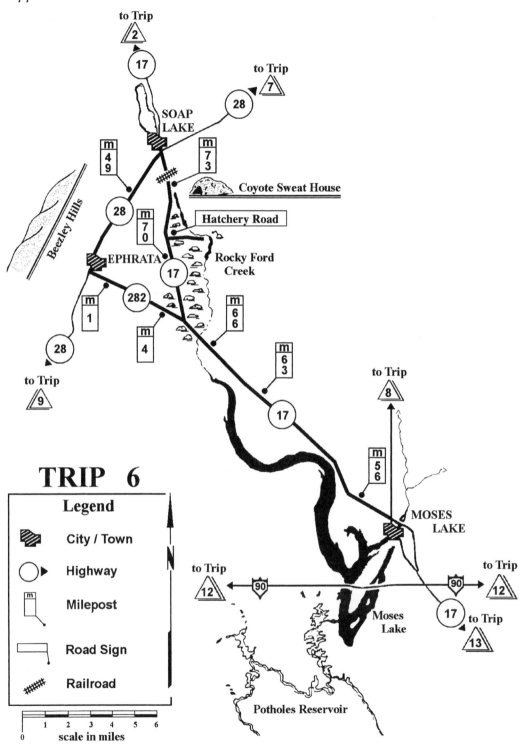

to Trip
△2

17

to Trip
▶ △7

28

SOAP
LAKE

m 4 9

m 7 3

Coyote Sweat House

28

m 7 0

Hatchery Road

EPHRATA

17

Rocky Ford
Creek

282

m 6 6

m 1

m 4

m 6 3

28

17

to Trip
△8

to Trip
△9

m 5 6

TRIP 6

Legend

MOSES
LAKE

City / Town

Highway

Milepost

Road Sign

Railroad

to Trip
△12

90

90

to Trip
△12

Moses
Lake

17
to Trip
▶ △13

N

1 2 3 4 5 6
0   scale in miles

Potholes Reservoir

44

Soap Lake to Moses Lake to Ephrata

TRIP 6

State Highways 17, 28 & 282

LENGTH: 32 MILES ONE WAY,
MILEPOSTS: 54–75 STATE HIGHWAY 17
          45–52 STATE HIGHWAY 28
          1–4 STATE HIGHWAY 282

This trip may originate from Soap Lake, Moses Lake, or Ephrata.

The depositional and erosional features illustrated along this route are easy to see as long as one can visualize the enormous magnitude of the floods and the fact that each segment of the event varied greatly in its volume and velocity of water and the amount of sand, rock, mud, and ice it carried. Imagine how in the same instant sand and gravel were laid down at one location while the flood gouged, plucked, and ripped out sediment and rock in an adjacent section. Flood deposits vary from fifty to 250 feet deep. As the waters raced, perhaps 100 miles per hour down the coulee, they emerged from the mouth of the Grand Coulee. And, as the waters swept out of the coulee mouth, they radiated and fanned out over the wide plain between Soap Lake and Moses Lake.

These Missoula floodwaters gouged and plucked out the rock formation in the Grand Coulee and dug deeply within the confined high velocity channel. As the waters emerged from the Grand Coulee, the Beezley Hills west of Ephrata forced the floodwater off of its eastern flank cutting a deep swath down through the valley where downtown Ephrata now lies.

As a side trip, travelers may drive northwest from Ephrata through the Beezley Hills to Sagebrush Flats. Eventually the Sagebrush Flats Road leads into Douglas County by way of Moses Coulee. Moses Coulee was an alternate flood route sculpted by the Missoula Floods but was also impacted by glacial activity in its upper reaches. The area is quite scenic and desolate.

South of Soap Lake, the floodwaters swept over onto a sediment-covered plain called the Quincy Basin. When the rapidly moving water burst out of the Grand Coulee at incredible speeds to meet the relatively flat plain, it must have caused a ricochet much like when a stone is skipped across water. Hydraulic engineers refer to this process as a hydraulic jump. As a result, the floodwaters did not simply drop their suspended load but threw the mass of suspended debris out of the coulee in a wide area several miles onto the flat between Soap Lake, Ephrata, and Moses Lake. After this initial ricochet, there was a rapid deceleration of the floodwater that varied in intensity from place to place and resulted in an almost chaotic distribution of rock sizes from sand and gravels to boulders tens of feet in diameter.

Two miles south of Soap Lake, lake bed sediments of the older sedimentary Ringold Formation remain intact under approximately thirty feet of coarse flood gravel. This demonstrates the lack of basal scouring or gouging in the area of the hydraulic jump.

MILEPOSTS 70–73

South of Soap Lake along State Highway 17, 6 miles directly below the mouth of the Grand Coulee where the flood met the flat, it dropped the very largest rocks (MP 70–73). A particularly unique or enigmatic boulder is located at the north end of Ephrata Lake just south of the railroad tracks (N MP 73) on State Highway 17. Referred to locally as the Coyote Sweathouse, the rock is a granite boulder which was hollowed out by floodwater before coming to rest in its present location during this last great flood event.

Erratics are rocks and dislocated soil masses not indigenous to the present location. Rock and soil carried by floodwaters in suspension or rolled and dislodged dropped out as the water lost its velocity and as icebergs enclosing this material melted. Ice-rafted boulders transported by Missoula Floods ended up in the Columbia Basin, Pasco area, Columbia Gorge near The Dalles and the Willamette Valley in Oregon. The granitic boulder rocks have been traced back to source areas north of Steamboat Rock near the city of Grand Coulee, in Montana, and the Canadian Rockies. These non-native rocks demonstrate the distances traveled, size, and depth of the flood and enormous volumes of water. Other types of rocks encountered are meta-sediments of quartzite, shale, gneiss, schist, and limestone. On State Highway 17, look for fine examples of erratics in the boulder field (MP 70–73).

Bouldery surface between Soap Lake and Ephrata

MILEPOSTS 49–50

On State Highway 28 boulders are also strewn helter-skelter over the surface along this route (between MP 49–50). Many of these boulders are now piled up by people trying to develop the land between Ephrata and Soap Lake.

North of State Highway 282 (MP 1) on the south edge of Ephrata, very thick gravel deposits cover Ringold Formation lake sediments. Between Rocky Ford Creek (MP 66–State Highway 17) and the Ephrata Airport (MP 4–State Highway 282) look for examples of water-transported basalt boulders scattered over the gravel bed. This marks the limit of super-velocity floodwater deposits that plunged out of the lower Grand Coulee.

As floodwater velocities decreased, the heaviest materials dropped out of the water first to become part of the bed load forming bar or terrace deposits. Farther away from Soap Lake as the channels fanned out, boulders became sparse and the bed load consisted of mostly coarse gravel and even sand farther away. The more finely textured material settled farther away from the coulee. The really fine-grained particles accumulated in backwater areas.

MILEPOSTS 2–3

Along the route between Ephrata and the junction of State Highway 282 with State Highway 17 (N & S MP 2–3) look for thousands of symmetrically rounded soil mounds that rise as much as two feet above the coarse sand and gravel base, are several feet across, and extend over hundreds of acres. Numerous explanations have been proposed to describe the mounds. They have been compared to a complex of similar-looking features called Mima Mounds near Tenino in western Washington that formed as glacial meltwater dropped sediment during the retreat of the last glacier and are arranged in crude geometric patterns. Another idea for the mounds formation includes the action of freezing and thawing cycles on the soil surface as part of a natural process known as ice wedging. Still other explanations include seismic activity, prolific rodent activity, wind and water erosion, or spotty accumulation of loess on the porous gravelly surface. These soil mounds also occur in areas of shallow basalt bedrock not subjected to flood erosion such as in the Beezley Hills north of Ephrata and north of Hartline. The origin of these soil mounds are not well understood and will remain an enigma until future studies determine how they formed.

MILEPOST 68

The meandering or curvy channels occupied by Moses Lake and Rocky Ford Creek (N MP 68 State Highway 17) reflect the persistence of a high velocity core of water that removed previously deposited flood sands and gravels. After leaving the Grand Coulee, the core of fast water entered and drained out of Moses Lake finally forcing its way to the Columbia River. This flushing action left the deeply cut channels and bars present as Rocky Ford Creek, Moses Lake, Crab Creek, and the Drumheller Channels.

After the floodwaters subsided, Crab Creek and Rocky Ford Creek now could flow freely through Moses Lake and the Drumheller Channels all the way to the Columbia River at Schawana.

Long and narrow elongated gravel bars are readily seen on many of these trips in some areas. Bar deposits are up to 150 feet high. It is typical to find many of these bar deposits positioned at mouths of streams or immediately downstream from natural obstructions. Gravel pits east and west of the State Highway 17 and 282 intersection illustrate the nature of the gravel bars at these locations. Inspect other local examples along State Highway 28 and State Highway 17 (MP 56, MP 57, and MP 63—State Highway 17 and MP 1—State Highway 28). These gravel pits are strategically located to take advantage of the thick, coarse-textured gravel for road building activities and are often good locations to look at profile characteristics of the flood deposits (cross bedding, strata, composition of the flood debris, etc.).

Along with the gravel, flood-deposited sands, which had been spread across the western floor of the Quincy Basin, were blown into sand dunes by prevailing westerly winds. The dunes migrated eastward across the deepest part of the Crab Creek channel to make a porous dam at Moses Lake's south end.

Symmetrical soil mounds, often referred to as patterned ground, Mima Mounds, or biscuit-scabland relief, dot the landscape along State Highway 282 (N MP 2) near Ephrata.

Soap Lake to the Grant-Lincoln County Line
Approx. 27 miles

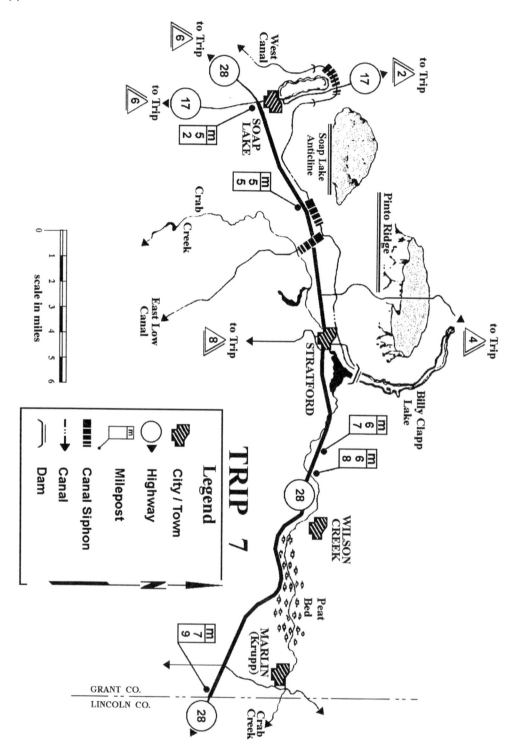

Soap Lake to the Grant-Lincoln County Line

TRIP 7

State Highway 28
LENGTH: 27 MILES ONE WAY, MILEPOSTS: 52–79

Begin at Soap Lake and head east toward Spokane.

MILEPOST 55

Between Soap Lake and Dry Coulee, the next canyon to the east, the road extends parallel to and south of the Soap Lake anticline, a prominent basalt hill (E MP 55).

At Stratford the highway zigzags across a small creek called Crab Creek. This Crab Creek valley was the site of another major flood outlet whose Missoula Floodwaters originated from the east. Prior to the Missoula Floods, Crab Creek cut a deep v-shaped valley into the basalt. The valley sides were mantled with loess (windblown silts). Since the pre-flood valley did not have the capacity to carry flood volumes, it over-flowed through low divides into adjacent valleys to the south creating multiple interconnected channels modifying the pre-existing topography.

Gravel bar deposits

A portion of the Missoula Flood crossed a divide from the Cheney-Palouse scablands to the east and plunged westward down Crab Creek. It widened the valley and filled the v-shaped bottom with coarse gravel leaving a relatively flat valley bottom with steep sides, especially the south side. Numerous bars of coarse sand and gravel with giant ripple marks atop them occur on this route. These features show, too, that this water had enormous velocity, volume, and depth to have been able to override the pre-existing landscape and create a new one (MP 67–68).

A significant portion of Crab Creek seeps out of Stratford Lake (also called Brook Lake) into a buried channel filled with coarse gravel and becomes the primary source of the spring water that rises as the source of Rocky Ford Creek (north and east of State Highway 17).

South and east of Wilson Creek and west of Marlin, on some maps known as Krupp, are extensive peat beds. This peat was formed in a marshy part of the scabland channel known as Crab Lake until 1907 when it was drained. Now Crab Creek flows through the entire length of the bog in a man-made channel.

Bedrock basalt columns lie in close proximity to deeper soils and wet areas associated with the Gloyd Seeps, an irrigation-induced wetland (10 NE and Stratford Road).

Stratford to Moses Lake
Approx. 22 miles

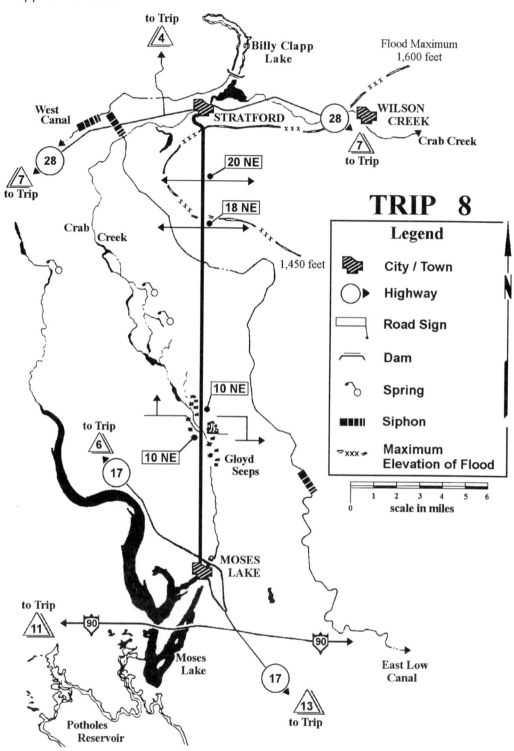

to Trip
4

Billy Clapp
Lake

Flood Maximum
1,600 feet

West
Canal

STRATFORD

28

WILSON
CREEK

Crab Creek

28

7
to Trip

7
to Trip

20 NE

18 NE

Crab   Creek

1,450 feet

TRIP   8

Legend

City / Town
Highway
Road Sign
Dam
Spring
Siphon
Maximum Elevation of Flood

0   1   2   3   4   5   6
scale in miles

10 NE

to Trip
6

17

10 NE

Gloyd
Seeps

MOSES
LAKE

to Trip
11

90

90

17

East Low
Canal

Moses
Lake

13
to Trip

Potholes
Reservoir

Stratford to Moses Lake

Stratford Road

LENGTH: 22 MILES ONE WAY

With the exception of the curve south of Stratford, the Stratford Road is straight as an arrow north to south. From the north end, enter the Stratford Road (E MP 62) from State Highway 28. From the south, proceed north of the city of Moses Lake on Stratford Road. There are no milepost signs on this route but the road numbers are clearly marked.

ROADS 20–22 NE

Climb out of the Crab Creek valley heading south from Stratford. Look for the loessial scarp that is at 1,400 to 1,450 elevation. The loess-covered rolling hills above the scarp represent another area untouched by the Missoula Floodwaters (roads 20 NE–22 NE).

ROAD 18 NE

The road passes through (unmarked) Broken Rock Coulee at road 18 NE about 1.5 miles north of the crossing over the East Low Canal. Coarse gravel up to 100 feet deep blankets the flood-scoured bedrock surface between here and Moses Lake.

ROAD 10 NE

The Gloyd Seeps are irrigation-induced wetlands established on shallow gravelly soils over basalt bedrock that is close to the surface (5 miles north of Moses Lake). Notice the relatively large number of trees and grasses that dominate the seep area.

Cross the Crab Creek channel again (road 10 NE) on the way to Moses Lake. Exposed basalt bedrock demonstrates that flood velocities were high enough to erode the rock at the same time the waters were slowing down to drop sand and gravel at lower velocity locations. This part of Crab Creek flowed only intermittently during spring runoff periods before the Columbia Basin Irrigation Project. Now there is enough irrigation water seeping into it to sustain it all year long.

Ephrata to Quincy to Crescent Bar

Approx. 25 miles

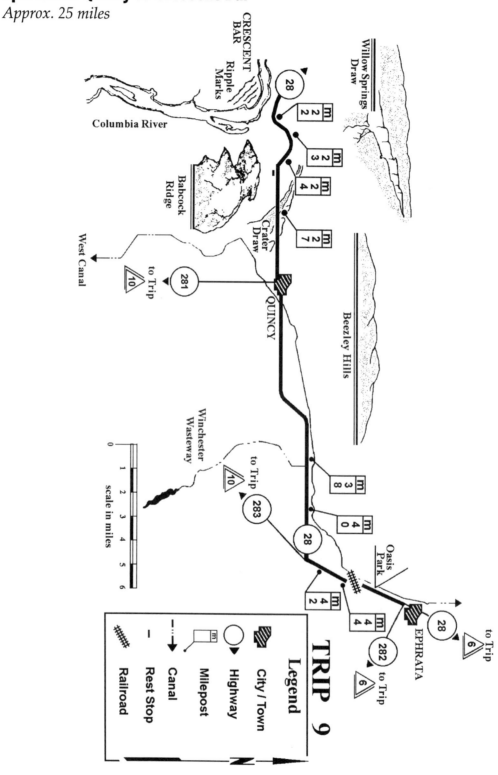

Ephrata to Quincy to Crescent Bar

TRIP
9

State Highway 28
LENGTH: 25 MILES ONE WAY, MILEPOSTS: 21–46

Start at Ephrata on State Highway 28 and drive to the southwest.

As you pass Oasis Municipal Park, note that the "oasis" is man-made. Seepage from the West Canal and deep percolation from irrigated orchards above the Canal to the northwest have created the oasis.

MILEPOSTS 42–44
South of Oasis Park, observe scabland channels that cut through a basalt anticline or hill. Further down the road, southwest of the railroad overpass (MP 42–44) notice a gravel bar southeast of the road deposited downstream from the basalt anticline at the overpass.

MILEPOSTS 38–40
Following State Highway 28 toward Quincy (MP 40) the exposed basalt scabland south of the road is overlain by very coarse gravel blanketed by a thin layer of loess. Further west the scabland rock surface (MP 38) abruptly ends and is overlaid by coarse sand.

The Winchester Wasteway, a concrete-lined chute from the West Canal to the valley bottom (MP 38), acts as an emergency outlet for the West Canal. Here, in the upper reaches of its course, the Winchester Wasteway follows the edge of the gravelly flood-wasted area to the east and the uneroded Ringold lake bed sediments to the west that are capped with flood-deposited sand and silt.

MILEPOST 27
Drive through Quincy and continue west. Three miles west of Quincy (W MP 27) State Highway 28 crosses swampy Crater Draw, which is a northwest flowing stream that passes through a series of lakes. This is a flood-carved channel outlet into the Columbia River and has a spectacular dry falls at its north end. At the highway crossing of Crater Draw (W MP 27) imagine the basalt bedrock that lies at a shallow depth under the highway. Crater Draw cuts more deeply into the basalt flows to the northwest as they rise to form the Beezley Hills on the north and Babcock Ridge

to the west. The stream flow was created by and is sustained by the discharge of ground water from under the irrigated lands of the Quincy Basin.

An earlier flood down the Columbia River valley is known to have entered the Columbia Basin in a southeasterly direction from the Columbia River as early as 75,000 years ago. The biggest Missoula Flood flowed northwesterly into the Columbia River; the different flow directions depended on the presence or absence of damming the Columbia River by the Okanogan lobe of the continental glaciers to the north.

MILEPOSTS 23–24

Descending the long grade to the Crescent Bar turnoff (Crescent Bar Recreational Area), the rock exposure along the road displays basalt lava flows with their distinctive columns and joint patterns (N MP 24) and opalized sedimentary interflow deposits (S MP 23). These flows were faulted and tilted downward to form the floor of Willow Springs Draw. As the land to the south rose and/or the land under the floor of the canyon sank, the lava flows were distorted and tilted to accommodate fault displacements in the underlying rock. Where the road traverses Willow Springs Draw (S & N MP 23) look for isolated exposures of flood gravels near its outlet.

Look across the Columbia River. The broad expanse of low land along the river's edge has a magnificent series of ripple marks. Excellent views of these giant ripple marks are on the west bar across the Columbia River from Crescent Bar (N MP 23). The ripple marks and waterways can also be seen quite dramatically from the air. The Columbia River at Crescent Bar forms a deeply cut curve as it runs south from Rock Island Dam (near Wenatchee). At Crescent Bar the river undercuts the left bank to form cliffs that diverted the flood downstream. The floodwaters deposited gravel and boulders on the ripple-marked bar on the inside of the curve as the flow was slowed and forced southward. The distance between the ripples and the height of the ripples is a measure of the flood's velocity, hundreds of feet deep at this location.

Relatively small accumulations of talus or loose rock dislodged during repeated freeze/thaw cycles are present at the foot of the cliffs on the east side of the Columbia River. Comparing this feature with the talus in the Grand Coulee leads to the speculation that the last flood to pass down the main stream of the Columbia River was significantly more recent than the last flood that occupied the Grand Coulee.

Ripple marks on Crescent Bar

There are other indications that a later flood occupied the Columbia River valley with physical evidence present from the mouth of the Methow River (north of Wenatchee) to Pasco. This could have happened with a final burst from Lake Missoula combined with a catastrophic breach of the Okanogan ice lobe barrier that released impounded water between Grand Coulee Dam and the Spokane River (known as Glacial Lake Columbia). Evidence for this flood comes from the presence of large boulder bars between Pateros and Wenatchee, the Malaga Slide area south of Wenatchee, the removal of a portion of the Crescent Bar ripple marks, the relatively small accumulation of talus along the Columbia River, and the relatively recent exposures of the Ringold sediments at White Bluffs across the river from Hanford.

Quincy to George to Ephrata

Approx. 28 miles

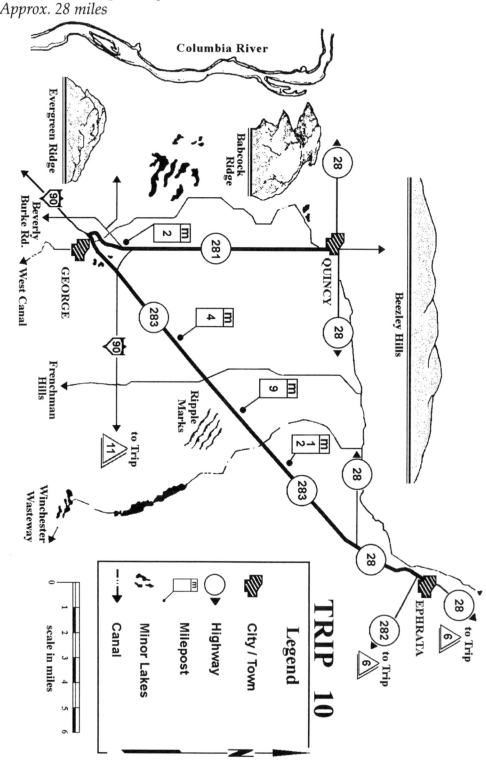

Quincy to George to Ephrata

State Highway 281, 283 & 28

LENGTH: 28 MILE ROUND TRIP LOOP,
MILEPOSTS: 1–10 STATE HIGHWAY 281
             1–12 STATE HIGHWAY 283
             41–46 STATE HIGHWAY 28

Drive south to George from Quincy on State Highway 281.

Some of the flood gravels at George and those west of Quincy were deposited by floodwaters moving in a southeasterly direction. Flood direction is indicated by the southeast tilt or dip of the deposits, which means an early smaller scale flood spilled over from the Columbia River. The flood carrying these deposits was the very first flood of any antiquity (50,000 years ago or more) to impact this area and it undoubtedly enlarged and shaped the Columbia River valley.

Floodwaters flowed around the north and south ends of Babcock Ridge west of Quincy and across all but the highest land on Evergreen Ridge west of George but never rose above 1,450 feet in elevation. The deposits consist of soil, caliche, and weathered basalt spread as cross-bedded layers dipping southeast and extending many miles eastward. Another indication of flood direction is the presence of "Vantage Sandstone" boulders now located approximately 2 miles southwest of Quincy. These boulders appear to have come in the floodwaters from Crater Draw about 6 miles to the northwest. Further indications of flood direction are the grain sizes in the flood sediments that decrease in size in a southeastward direction helping to confirm the theory that the flood-eroded gaps through Babcock Ridge originated from the Columbia River valley.

MILEPOSTS 4–5, STATE HIGHWAY 281

On State Highway 281 (MP 4-5), the view to the west reveals the flood's thorough excavation of the scabland between Babcock Ridge and Evergreen Ridge. In some deposits there is evidence that earlier east-flowing floods and the biggest west-flowing floods overlapped.

MILEPOST 2, STATE HIGHWAY 281

Some of the best exposed remnants of these early floods on the

Columbia Plateau are found in caliche-capped flood gravel deposits at a sanitary landfill. From State Highway 281, turn right onto the Beverly Burke Road (MP 2). Cross the West Canal and turn right on 1 NW and follow it 0.3 miles to the landfill site. In this area, the oldest event is recorded as a flood gravel containing boulders up to three feet in diameter. This boulder-filled gravel bed was then covered by a wind-deposited loess soil cemented by calcium carbonate called caliche. The caliche forms in areas of dry climate and low rainfall and occurs where water evaporates from the soil causing salts to precipitate out in a porous zone. In places, cementation extends several inches into the underlying gravel. Immediately under the caliche, the gravels have severely weathered and are broken into small fragments. However, the gravel below a depth of 10 feet shows no evidence of weathering.

Go east on Interstate Freeway 90 to the State Highway 283 interchange and toward Ephrata on State Highway 283.

MILEPOSTS 6–9, STATE HIGHWAY 283

Note the dune-like or ripple mark topography carved by floodwater action on the flood-deposited sands (between MP 6–9).

The Winchester Wasteway (MP 9) on State Highway 283 winds along a shallow valley to the Potholes Reservoir. The wasteway is a major drainage for ground water derived from the irrigation operations in the north central portion of the Quincy Basin. This shallow valley formed at the interface between two distinctive flood phases. On the eastern side of the valley deposits were laid down by the southwest-flowing high velocity floods coming out of the Grand Coulee. Here, there are up to 100 feet of very coarse, permeable gravels. On the other side of the valley, the land to the west is left with a thin mantle of flood-deposited sands and silts dropped by a much earlier flood that originated from the Columbia River and was later covered by low velocity flooding from the Grand Coulee.

During each flood, low lying basins were briefly filled up as the water backed behind large ridges before draining out into the Columbia River Gorge through Wallula Gap near Pasco. Each flood produced a short-lived lake or series of lakes. Some of these lakes may have covered more than 2,000 square miles with maximum elevations of 1,200 feet south of the Frenchman Hills and 1,355 feet north of the Frenchman Hills and south of the Grand Coulee.

Ancient Lakes area between Quincy and George, west of State Highway 281.

Vantage to the Adams County Line

Approx. 56 miles

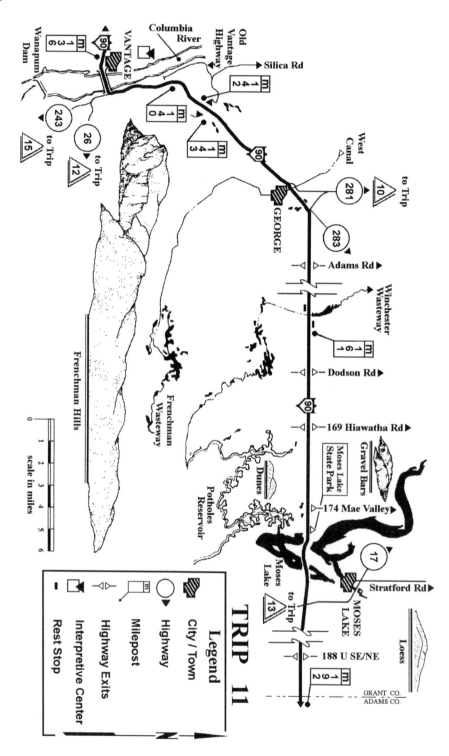

Vantage to George to Moses Lake to the Grant-Adams County Line

Interstate Freeway 90

LENGTH: 56 MILES ONE WAY, MILEPOSTS: 136–192

MILEPOST 136

A trip through this area would be incomplete without a stop at the Ginkgo Petrified Forest State Park on the Columbia River at Vantage. On the west side of the Columbia River, turn into Vantage from Interstate Freeway 90 (at exit 136) and proceed through town to the state park interpretive center. Petrified trees and fossil leaves indicate this once was a forested landscape interspersed with lakes, streams, and marshes. The park sets aside a portion of this rich petrified flora.

From the Vantage Bridge (east on Interstate 90) the freeway crosses the westernmost edge of what is called the Frenchman Hills anticline. This low range of hills divides the Quincy Basin on the north from the Royal Slope and Crab Creek valley on the south.

MILEPOSTS 139–142

Westbound only, a scenic viewpoint (S MP 140) shows off the Columbia River Gorge and gives a grand view of Wanapum Lake on the Columbia River. The lava flows on the west side of the river dip to the south, which is the southern limb of the Frenchman Hills anticline. From this vantage point the effect of the floodwaters clearly show that the top of the anticline is heavily gouged and incised. Bench-like features can be seen on both the west and east sides of the Columbia River where weak zones in between lava flows allowed the floodwaters to undermine overlying flows.

For eastbound travelers, a scenic viewpoint is provided off the east lanes of Interstate 90 (MP 139). Besides viewing a portion of Wanapum Lake on the Columbia River, there is a display of wild horse statues commemorating the roundup of wild horses that took place during the early days of settlement in Grant County.

On the way to George, diatomaceous earth beds stand exposed on the left side (north) as the freeway curves eastward over the divide into the Quincy Basin (N MP 142).

MILEPOSTS 143–147

Four miles southwest of George off Interstate Freeway 90 turn on Exit 143 at the Silica Road interchange. Pass under the freeway (north) and turn west (left) onto the old Vantage Highway (U. S. 10) across from the North Frontage Road. This is a good side trip to look at the planes of weakness in the basalt bedrock that determined the erosional flood patterns that were created by the floodwaters. Imagine a series of cataracts and waterfalls that covered the area as floodwaters churned through here on their way into the Columbia River gorge. Other flood outlets included the Drumheller Channels south of Moses Lake, Potholes Coulee (southwest of Quincy), and Crater Draw west of Quincy. This side trip is also an excellent place to observe the three-tier rock characteristics typical of most basalt flows. Be sure to look for the vesicular surface, the blocky-structured center or entablature, and long vertical columns known as the colonnade. Outstanding examples of columnar basalt may be seen here.

Basalt columns on Old Vantage Highway (U. S. Highway 10)

Before returning to the freeway, another interesting side trip is to check out the Silica Road diatomaceous earth pits. Diatomaceous earth consists of silica-rich shells of microscopic plants exposed within interflow sediments between basalt flows. These very ancient sediments were exposed by flood erosion. The pits have been left open since being mined during World War I for oil filters on battleships.

The freeway (MP 147) cuts through Evergreen Ridge exposing layers of the sedimentary Ringold Formation.

Driving east from George, Interstate Freeway 90 passes through a nearly flat basin. No bedrock is exposed in this stretch. All bedrock is buried under sand and gravel laid down by multiple Missoula Floods. The floods also partially eroded into Ringold Formation lake sediments.

MILEPOSTS 160–162

The Winchester Wasteway (MP 160) follows a shallow valley to the Potholes Reservoir. The wasteway is a major drainage for ground water derived from the irrigation operations in the north central portion of the Quincy Basin. This shallow valley formed at the interface between two distinctive flood deposits. On the eastern side of the valley, deposits were laid down by the southwest-flowing high velocity floods coming out of the Grand Coulee. Here, there are up to 100 feet of very coarse gravels. On the other side of the valley, the land to the west is left with a thin mantle of flood-deposited sands and silts dropped by a much earlier flood that originated from the Columbia River and later covered by low velocity flooding from the Grand Coulee. The sands and silts overlie Ringold Formation lake sediments.

At the Winchester Wasteway Rest Area (MP 161–162) located 6 miles east of George, the flood debris changes from gravel to medium-sized sands. This transition represents a bed load deposit of two different floods. An early flood from the Columbia River overflowed west to east out of and up over the intervening ridge. The older deposit is probably more than 50,000 years old because it is associated with channels on Babcock Ridge that were eroded into and later mantled by loess. The gravelly deposits of this earlier flood are overlaid with the sandy deposits of the later great Missoula Flood. The sand contains caliche pebbles eroded from some of the earlier flood gravels and/or from Ringold Formation lake sediments.

East of the Winchester Wasteway, two sandy and gravelly flood deposits overlie the fine-textured ancient lake and stream deposits of Ringold age (greater than 3 million years old).

MILEPOSTS 169–175

Changing dynamics of the floodwaters are well illustrated along this route as sand and gravel deposits were alternately dropped. Between the Winchester Wasteway and Mae Valley (Exits 174–175) floodwaters dropped coarse sandbar hills tens of feet thick and miles wide and long. Two enormous gravel bars can be seen north of the freeway in Mae Valley and just to the east of the freeway bridge that crosses Moses Lake.

Also, look for sand and gravel bars as indications of how floodwater velocities and volumes fluctuated. Both the Hiawatha Valley (Exit 169)

Gigantic elongated gravel bars are visible from the freeway

and Mae Valley (Exit 174) are underlain with large gravelly bed load deposits. Columbia Basin Irrigation Project water, which fills Potholes Reservoir to the south, also causes ground water and lake levels to rise and fall in the Hiawatha and Mae Valley areas.

Post-flood sand dunes blew west to east to form Moses Lake by blocking the Crab Creek flood channel. The dunes also continue eastward for several miles. Moses Lake State Park (MP 175) is located on some of these dunes.

MILEPOST 188

Proceeding east toward the Adams County line, notice the relief is characterized by more rounded gently sloping hills rather than the steep-sided rock walls of the scablands. This is because the floodwater slowed due to reduced depth, gradient, and velocity. East of the Warden interchange (MP 188), Interstate Freeway 90 rises above the maximum flood level (approximately 12 miles east of the East Low Canal location) and the rolling hills reflect the lack of scouring action. Here lie untouched thick layers of wind-deposited loess.

High elevations left scattered patches of land untouched by the floodwater in several places north and east of Moses Lake with undisturbed loessial soil lying on top of the basalt. Most of the dry cropland east of the East Low Canal to the Adams County line was untouched by the floods and in many areas the loess is as much as thirty feet thick.

The East Low Canal follows the 1,250-foot elevation contour, 100 feet below the maximum flood level.

MILEPOSTS 191–192

Also, east of Moses Lake to the Adams County line (MP 191–192), slack water deposits, which are fine-grained bedded sediments dropped when floodwaters slowed down and backed up, may be seen on the level flats. At the Adams County line, Interstate Freeway 90 crosses a system of coulees that carried more languidly flowing floodwaters. These coulees were not scoured to bedrock but fed the slack water lakes with finer-grained sediments.

Fossilized trees dominate the landscape at Ginkgo Petrified Forest State Park in Vantage.

Vantage Bridge to the Adams County Line

Approx. 31 miles

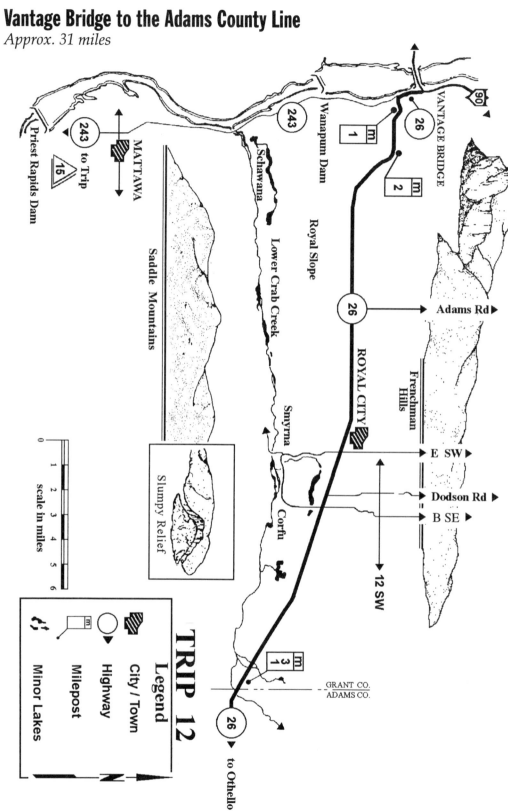

Vantage Bridge to the Grant-Adams County Line

South and east towards Othello on State Highway 26

LENGTH: 31 MILES ONE WAY, MILEPOSTS: 1–31

From the Vantage Bridge (Interstate 90), turn south and east along State Highway 26 up the hill through unmarked Sand Hollow and onto the Royal Slope toward Royal City.

MILEPOST 1

Pillow basalts occur when lava flows enter water. Just after turning east on State Highway 26 (E MP 1), look in the roadcut north of the road for a good example of pillow basalts. The pillows are rounded or semi-rounded dark basalt nodules with orange hues peppering the space between nodules.

MILEPOST 2

The road moves through an area of loess, cemented sand and gravel and colluvium overlain by caliche (MP 2). This gravelly deposit is evidence of a flood event that occurred more than 50,000 years ago. Also seen on either side of the road in this vicinity are flood gravels with angled foreset beds (inclined cross-beds) indicating coarse bed load deposits at the bottom of the floodwater.

MILEPOST 24

Traveling east between Royal City and Dodson Road, look south (S MP 24). In the distance a light-colored bluff stands exposed at the toe of the Saddle Mountains. This bluff consists of sedimentary water-deposited lake beds of the Ringold Formation. Ringold sediments were laid down and covered portions of both the Frenchman Hills and Saddle Mountains but were exposed and partially removed in the course of floodwater action. The toe or bottom of the bluff between Smyrna and Corfu was taken off by flood erosion.

For an additional side trip, drive south from Royal City (State Highway 26 on road E SW) to Smyrna and east to Corfu. The road is paved to Smyrna and gravelled to Corfu (B SE). What is intriguing about this route are the colorful Ringold Formation sediments that overlie dark basalt flows along the north edge of the Saddle Mountains. Also, the route traverses a portion of a gigantic ancient landslide that originated in the Saddle Mountains.

At about 7 miles east of Royal City, look south at the flank of the Saddle Mountains (road C SE) where a giant landslide collapsed the entire north slope of the mountains into a huge disorganized pile of earth. Also, observe the notch or col in the crest of the Saddle Mountains where the back of the slide notched the skyline. This slide occurred after the flood-water surging out of the Drumheller Channels scooped out the supporting toe of the original slope as the floodwater was forced westward down lower Crab Creek.

Flood waters created the Drumheller Channels where the Frenchman Hills anticline dips through a low gap in the landscape. Sedimentary lake-laid deposits associated with the Ringold Formation were removed and fractured basalt was eroded and plucked as floodwaters raced and es-caped to the south. As the water cut its path, its impact was lessened as it entered the deep sediment-laden east-west synclinal trough occupied by the Othello Basin. Between the Frenchman Hills and the north edge of the

Bouldery surfaces, alkali lakes, basalt rock outcrops and a network of low el-evation exposed basalt channels thread their way through this landscape (W MP 31) along lower Crab Creek.

Visualize how molten lava engulfed a pool of water causing rapid cooling which created the "pillows" in the basalt rock seen exposed along the roadway. (E MP 1).

Saddle Mountains, hundreds of feet of sediment were removed and lesser volumes of basalt exposed small scabland channels (MP 31–west of MP 30) as the floodwaters raced across the basin. Notice the labyrinth of scabland channels, shallow soils with bouldery surfaces, and basalt outcrops along this section of lower Crab Creek. From its juncture with State Highway 26, the floodwaters ripped out the toe slope and hugged the north edge of the Saddle Mountains as it continued westward down lower Crab Creek dropping 100 feet in 25 miles before outletting into the Columbia River.

Moses Lake to the Adams County Line
Approx. 20 miles

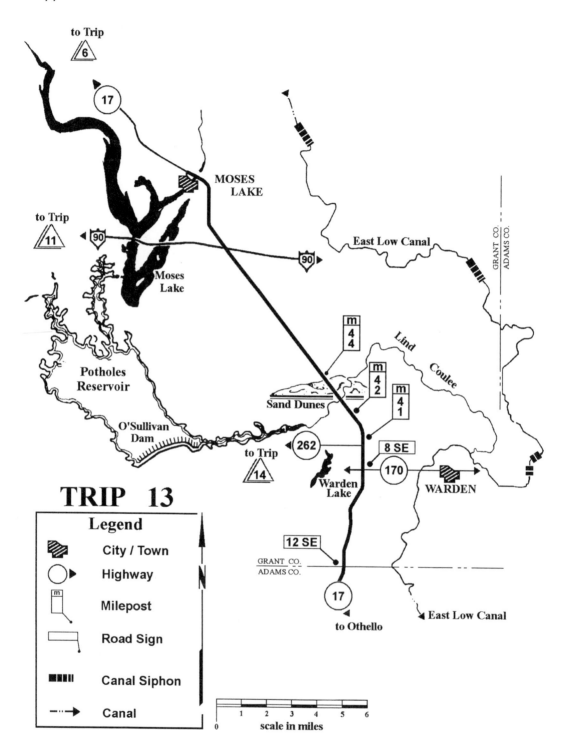

to Trip
6

17

MOSES
LAKE

to Trip
11

90

90

East Low Canal

GRANT CO.
ADAMS CO.

Moses
Lake

Lind
Coulee

m
4
4

Potholes
Reservoir

m
4
2

m
4
1

Sand Dunes

O'Sullivan
Dam

262

8 SE

170

to Trip
14

Warden
Lake

WARDEN

TRIP 13

Legend

City / Town

Highway

N

Milepost

Road Sign

Canal Siphon

Canal

12 SE

GRANT CO.
ADAMS CO.

17

East Low Canal

to Othello

1 2 3 4 5 6
0
scale in miles

Moses Lake to the Grant-Adams County Line

TRIP 13

State Highway 17

LENGTH: 20 MILES ONE WAY, MILEPOSTS: 36–56

This route runs south from the city of Moses Lake on State Highway 17 to the Grant County-Adams County Line.

MILEPOSTS 42–45

State Highway 17 passes by the eastern edge of a large expanse of dune sands that originated as flood sands first deposited 30 miles to the west. The dunes were subsequently wind-driven east to impound Moses Lake. Just south of where State Highway 17 passes over Lind Coulee, notice that the sand dunes cross the highway (MP 43–45).

Again at Lind Coulee (E MP 42) a rare view of the Ringold Formation lake sediments lies exposed in the southeastern cut bank. These fine-grained lake sediments are 3–8 million years old. From these sediments a large assortment of fossils have been recovered including freshwater mollusks, fish, and vertebrate fossils. Capping the Ringold Formation

Ringold Formation sediments may be seen in cutbanks east of the bridge that crosses the Lind Coulee wasteway

sediments is a white layer of caliche. The caliche is a typical desert by-product that accumulated through a long period of dry climatic conditions.

Imagine the Lind Coulee shoreline (further east near the town of Warden) where prehistoric Native Americans hunted and butchered bison along the riparian area nearly 10,000 years ago.

MILEPOSTS 36–41

Besides an isolated exposure of Ringold Formation sediment layers, erosion and deposition associated with the catastrophic floods has removed nearly all other deposits here. Evidence that the floods came through this area is indicated by many feet of fine-grained slack water deposits (MP 36–41). These deposits formed in quiet water conditions as the floodwaters backed up before draining out into the Columbia River.

Another interesting side trip will take the traveler to view close up a basalt dike exposed during the course of floodwater action near Warden. Turn east onto 8 SE (State Highway 170) off State Highway 17 (S MP 40) towards Warden and after 2.4 miles turn south along the west edge of the East Low Canal. The canal road is gravelled. Drive for about 2 miles and park. Walk out onto the elevated basalt lava knob off the right shoulder of the road. This is actually a lava dike that stands above most of the other landscape features. The fractured jointed rock has tiny isolated vesicles or voids uniformly distributed throughout the massive formation indicative of an intrusive lava dike that rose from the earth's mantle.

At road 12 SE, also called Providence Road, enter Adams County (S MP 36). Look off to the west for a glimpse of an elongated hill known as Jackass Mountain. The hill is actually an isolated remnant of one of the first floods (tens of thousands of years ago) to have dumped gravel in the area. What is interesting is that it escaped complete removal of the largest floods since it is capped with a layer of semi-cemented caliche that resisted flood erosion.

Caliche capped gravels overlie fine textured lacustrine sediments correlated to the Ringold Formation. This elongated bar is called Jackass Mountain and may be seen off to the west on road 12 SE.

O'Sullivan Dam Road to Potholes Reservoir

Approx. 17 miles

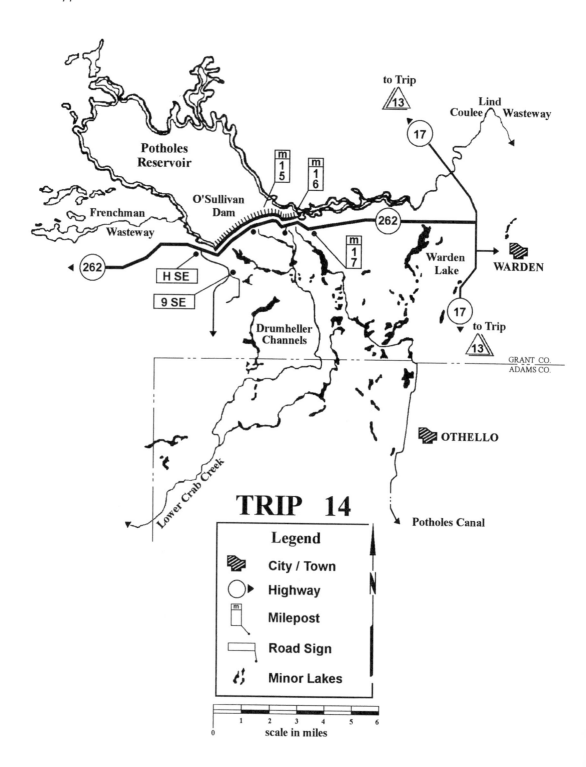

O'Sullivan Dam Road to Potholes Reservoir

TRIP 14

West on State Highway 262

LENGTH: 17 MILES ONE WAY, MILEPOSTS: 7–24

Begin at the intersection with State Highway 17 (N MP 41).

The O'Sullivan Dam Road or State Highway 262 crosses an area severely scoured and gouged by floodwaters. South of Potholes Reservoir, the Columbia National Wildlife Refuge contains some of the area's starkest natural beauty in contrast to fertile uneroded lands north and east of Moses Lake.

Completed in 1949, O'Sullivan Dam was constructed with a compacted earth-filled core. The dam closes off drainage from the lowest point in the Quincy Basin where lower Crab Creek flows through an incised scabland. This low point in the topography was selected for the dam because it effectively controls all water draining from the north and stores it for re-use. The reservoir collects runoff from the 4,000 square miles of the upper Crab Creek watershed, which extends from the Quincy Basin on the west to the town of Sprague near Spokane on the east. Surface and ground water discharges from all Columbia Basin Irrigation Project activities as well as natural surface runoff in this entire area can thus be captured and used to irrigate lands further south. Potholes Canal takes water from the Potholes Reservoir to the southern part of the Project area. The Potholes Canal Headworks has been modified to generate electricity as it discharges water into the Potholes Canal.

MILEPOSTS 15–18

The Drumheller Channels are an exceptionally picturesque series of scabland channels pocketed with seep lakes (S MP 15–18). These seep lakes, enhanced by irrigation project development, have created a prime recreational area.

Just west of Mardon Resort, turn south up the hill on road H SE. Before cresting the hill (at 1.5 miles from the intersection), turn left onto road 9 SE and park after about 0.3 miles. Walk east to get a spectacular view of the Drumheller Channels. As you walk observe that the soil becomes

Drumheller Channels

shallow and finally gives way to a surface nearly devoid of soil cover. This is the margin of the flood-eroded scabland; the soil-covered lands escaped the flood scour. Look east across the Drumheller Channels and imagine an enormous flood surging southward over all the landscape below you. In the process of creating the Drumheller Channels, the Missoula Floodwaters removed the whole east end of the Frenchman Hills. The Drumheller Channels cut 300 feet into the basalt, cover more than 50 square miles, and they are approximately 9 miles wide.

Scan the view from the Highway 262 (MP 15–18) on top of O'Sullivan Dam looking into the channels and note how the lava flows dip gently downward forming the southern flank of the Frenchman Hills anticline. It is interesting to realize that the magnitude of the great flood was so large that at the same time the waters surged around this eastern edge of the Frenchman Hills here in the Drumheller Channels, the same flood pushed around the western edge of the hills along the Columbia River 30 miles away (MP 140).

While in this area, the traveler can drive into or through the Columbia National Wildlife Refuge pausing at any of the scabland lakes south of O'Sullivan Dam. This is an opportunity to view the beauty and starkness of the Drumheller Channels gouged out by the Missoula

Floods. The Refuge has many access points from State Highway 262 and north of State Highway 26 (north of Othello).

From the H SE turnoff, travel west past Potholes State Park. On the north edge of the Frenchman Hills the flood volume and velocity were relatively smaller compared to the main rush of water that scoured out the Drumheller Channels to the east. In this area (MP 11) caliche may be seen exposed in roadcuts. Further to the west along the road (east MP 7) at the intersection of State Highway 262 and Frenchman Hills Road are several scattered ice rafted bouldery erratics. These granite boulders are several feet in diameter and are identical to granite that lies along the western edge of the lake that dammed Glacial Lake Missoula.

Several ice rafted granite erratic boulders lie next to the road at the intersection of State Highway 262 and the Frenchman Hills Road (east MP 7)

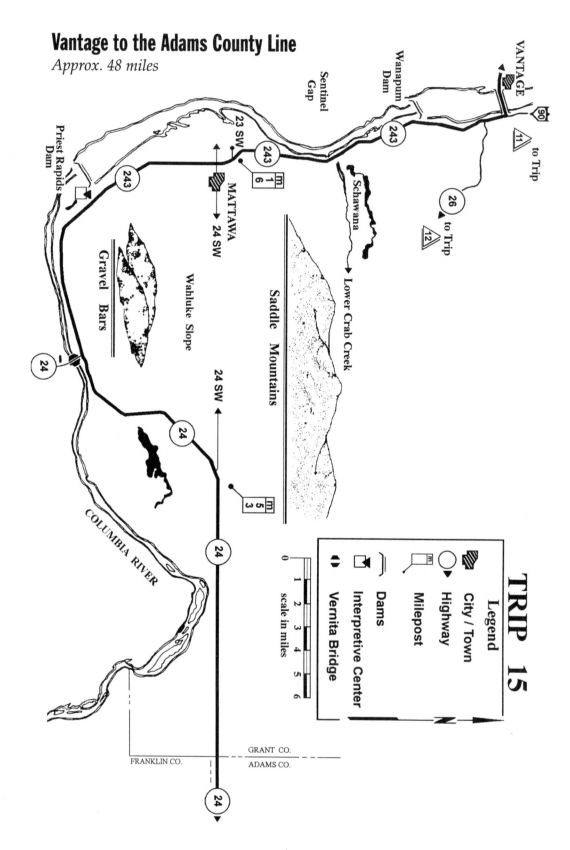

Vantage to Mattawa to the Grant-Adams County Line

TRIP 15

South on State Highway 243, and east on State Highway 24

LENGTH: 48 MILES ONE WAY,

MILEPOSTS: 1–28 STATE HIGHWAY 243

45–65 STATE HIGHWAY 24

Proceed south from Vantage on State Highway 243 towards Mattawa. Or, turn west onto State Highway 24 just south of Othello.

At Schawana, floodwater flowing west along Crab Creek merged with floodwaters in the Columbia River valley. The water then passed southward through Sentinel Gap in the Saddle Mountains to enter the Pasco Basin at Mattawa. From there, the flood forced its way through Wallula Gap south of Pasco, down the Columbia River, and eventually out to the Pacific Ocean.

On State Highway 243 flood erosion along the road south to Priest Rapids Dam was confined to areas along the Columbia River proper except where the water produced large eddy gravel bar deposits in the area around Mattawa. Scoured exposures of basalt in the gorge and flood bar deposits characterize this area of the Columbia River.

MILEPOST 16

Of particular interest are features near Sentinel Gap (MP 16). From this milepost, proceed to road 23 SW and park. Looking north, observe the edge of the Saddle Mountains. The basalt flows in the mountains rise gently to the north toward the mountain crest. The white sedimentary bed close to the top is a fine-grained volcanic ash from a very ancient volcanic eruption millions of years ago. The composition of this ash is chemically unique to this area. During the construction of Priest Rapids Dam, the ash was added to the cement in order to increase its strength and its resistance to saline and acidic solutions. It also reduced the amount of cement needed. Volcanic ash with these valuable chemical properties is known as a Pozzolan material, named after Pozzouli, Italy, where this type of ash was first used. So, the addition of this material made a very high quality concrete at a reduced cost.

MILEPOSTS 53–65

On State Highway 24 (MP 53) look north at the Saddle Mountains. Wahatis Peak is the highest point of the mountain. Compare the very smooth and level mountain crest to the west with the irregular, heavily eroded, skyline to the east. Even though the mountain is higher on the eastern part, it is much older than the western part.

Look to the south (MP 53) and imagine how the Missoula Floodwaters removed all the land between the White Bluffs (along the river) and Manastash Ridge to the west in the Columbia River Valley.

From here (MP 53–65) east to the county line, flood deposits blanket the surface, except along the Columbia River to the south, where older fine-grained Ringold Formation sediments are exposed and can be seen sloughing off into the river.

Sentinel Gap (in the background) on the Columbia River north of Mattawa, afforded the Missoula floodwater with an outlet through the Saddle Mountains. The stacked boulders (in the foreground) attest to the magnitude of the floods (S MP 15 SH 243).

84

Glossary of Frequently Used Geological Terms

ALLUVIAL—stream-deposited sediments

ANTICLINE—a convex or domed feature in the rock strata. These lava rock features in Grant County are often highly fractured, which made them more susceptible to catastrophic flood damage

BAR—masses of sand, gravel, and boulders dropped by floodwater

BASALT—a rock that started as molten lava, a typical feature of all igneous rocks, that erupts through non-explosive fissures or cracks in the earth's crust. Basalt lava spreads out, cools, and builds up layer upon layer. It is distinguished by black or brown color resulting from a dominance of dark minerals

BED LOAD DEPOSITS—coarse textured soil, gravel, boulders, and other debris rolled along the bottom of a body of moving water and dropped by it when velocity decreases

BOULDER—rock-sized particle greater than 24 inches in diameter

CALICHE—white-colored calcium carbonate cemented deposits are created as water soluble minerals precipitate out of solution and are typical of dry climates

CAST—an impression or mold created by the replacement of animal or plant parts with minerals or other rock forming elements

CLAY—a very fine-grained sediment, smaller than silt- or sand-sized particles less than .002 millimeters in diameter

COLONNADE—complex of basalt columns that form the base of a lava flow

COLLUVIUM—loose, often angular rock, and sediment that moves, primarily by gravity, down a slope and is deposited along the toe or base of a cliff; see talus

COLUMNAR—cooling feature typical of basalt lava flows that fracture into polygonal-shaped vertical columns

COULEE—steep-sided canyon or gulch eroded by a stream much larger than the stream now occupying it

CROSS-BEDDING OR FORESET BEDS—These layered water-deposited sediments are inclined or offset from the (horizontal) primary planes of stratification, or are the leading edge of deposits that actively cut across a previously deposited layer. They are used as indicators of changing current directions in a flood or river

DIATOMACEOUS EARTH—buff-colored silica-rich shells of microscopic plants called diatoms lived and died in fresh (or salt) water. Their fossilized remnants accumulated as thick layers of sediment between basalt layers

DIKE—molten lava that erupts through fissures or cracks in the earth's crust and cuts up through several lava flow layers and rises to the surface

DIP—sediments or rock features that are offset or inclined from the horizontal

ENTABLATURE—internal mid-section of a lava flow consisting of unorganized and/or blocky fracture patterns

EPOCH—a unit of geologic time which is a subdivision of a period

ERA—geologic time units are subdivided into segments using a world wide classification system. The era is the highest order that is divided into periods and epochs.

ERRATIC—non-native rocks and soil carried in icebergs and/or by moving water and deposited away from place of origin

EXTRUSIVE—refers to the movement of molten lava from deep in the earth that rises to the earth's surface, causing it to cool very quickly

FAUNA—animals

FISSURE—vertical crack or narrow break in the earth's crust through which liquid lava rises or erupts out onto the surface

FLORA—plants

GLACIER—large mass of moving ice

GRANITE—rock whose mineral components cooled very slowly beneath the earth's surface before being exposed to weathering and erosion; this rock is distinguished by its light gray color and predominance of quartz crystal inclusions

GRAVEL—rock particle greater than 2 millimeters in size and smaller than 24 inches in diameter

INTERBED—water deposited sediments laid down (stratified) between two other distinct layers

INTERFLOW—zone between successive lava flows in which sediments are laid

INTRUSIVE—molten (magma) lava that rises from below the earth's surface and solidifies before it reaches the surface

LACUSTRINE—sediments deposited in a lake

LAVA—liquid or fluid rock that rises from the earth's interior through volcanoes or fissures in the crust

LOESS—windblown (aeolian) material made up predominantly of particles that are primarily silt size (.05 - .1 mm). Where the loess covered surface was untouched by the Missoula Floods, there are several feet of soil.

METASEDIMENT—water-laid deposits transformed into rock through intense heat and/or pressure

OROGENY—mountain-building processes

PERIOD—unit of geologic time that is a subdivision of an era; see era and epoch

PILLOW BASALTS—rounded masses or "pillow-shaped" nodules of basalt rock formed when the molten lava came into contact with a water body and cooled quickly

RINGOLD FORMATION—light colored white, brown, or orange deposits named for the White Bluffs exposures near the town of Ringold on the Columbia River north of Pasco, Washington; these finely layered lake and stream deposits overly basalt lava throughout the Columbia Plateau and are associated with a variety of fossilized fish and animals

RIPPLE MARKS—topographic feature created by moving water that ripples the strata on the bottom of the stream and lake bed

SCABLANDS—exclusively reserved for lava relief in the Pacific Northwest created by the gouging, plucking, and scouring floodwaters that removed soil and rock and left a variety of erosional features including shallow soils, rocky canyons, channels, and coulees

SILL—similar to a dike in that it originates as molten lava that cuts up between existing lava flows. However, sills do not rise to the surface. Sill rock has internal features including crystals that cooled very slowly and isolated holes or voids scattered through it indicative of lava that did not come into contact with the air at the surface.

SILT—medium-sized particles between .05–.002 millemeters in diameter; larger than clay-sized particles and smaller than sand

SIPHON—a specially designed upright pipe or inverted canal channel that forces pressure on the water within it to move up or down between points. Siphons in the Columbia Basin Irrigation Project are called "inverted" siphons because the water is conveyed downward and then up to outlet in a canal that is at a slightly lower elevation than the water at the inlet, thereby maintaining the desired flow through the pipe.

STRATIGRAPHY—the study of layered deposits accumulated by water or lava

TALUS—loose angular rock called colluvium along coulees and canyons with steep-sided rocky slopes that is the result of freezing and thawing activity; this material breaks off the nearly sheer rock walls and accumulates on the toe slopes beneath the cliffs

VARVES—thinly bedded layers that represent yearly accumulations of fine-textured lake sediments

VESICLES—rounded or spherical holes at and near the surface of a lava flow; they form from gas bubbles in molten extruded magma entrapped by the solidification process resulting from the cooling of lava exposed to surface temperatures

References

Allen, John Elliot, Marjorie Burns, and Sam C. Sargent. *Cataclysms on the Columbia: A Layman's Guide to Features Produced by the Catastrophic Bretz Floods in the Pacific Northwest.* Portland: Timber Press, 1986.

Alt, David D., and Donald W. Hyndman. *Roadside Geology of Washington.* Missoula: Mountain Press Publishing Co., 1984.

Baker, Victor R. "Paleohydrology and Sedimentology of Lake Missoula Flooding in Eastern Washington." *Geological Society of America Special Paper 144* (1973): 1–79.

Baker, Victor R., Bruce N. Bjornstad, Alan J. Busacca, Karl R. Fecht, E. P. Kiver, Ula L. Moody, James G. Rigby, D. F. Stradling, and Ann M. Tallman "Quaternary Geology of the Columbia Plateau." Chapter 8. *The Geology of North America.* Vol. K-2, Quaternary Nonglacial Geology: Coterminus U. S. The Geological Society of America. 1991

Bennett, William Alfred Glenn. *Saline Lake Deposits in Washington.* Washington. Division of Mines and Geology, Bulletin no. 49. Olympia, 1962.

Berg, Andrew W. "Formation of Mima Mounds: A Seismic Hypothesis." *Geology*, March 1990.

Bretz, J Harlen. "The Lake Missoula Floods and the Channeled Scablands." *Journal of Geology* 77 (1969): 505–543.

Bretz, J Harlen, H T. U. Smith, and George E. Neff "Channeled Scabland of Washington: New Data and Interpretations." *Bulletin of the Geological Society of America.* Vol 67. pp 957-1049. 1956

Fecht, Karl R., Stephen P. Reidel, and Ann M. Tallman. "Paleodrainage of the Columbia River System on the Columbia Plateau of Washington State—A Summary." In *Selected Papers on the Geology of Washington,* edited by J. Eric Schuster. Washington. Division of Geology and Earth Resources, Bulletin no. 77. Olympia, 1987: 219–248.

Gentry, Herman, *Soil Survey of Grant County, Washington.* Field work by Herman Gentry, Dale L. Olson, James C. Michael, Mark S. Amara, Larry W. Ross, Michael L. Mrachek, Willard A. Call, Dale E. Snyder, and James W. Pahl. Soil Conservation Service. National Cooperative Soil Survey. U. S. Department of Agriculture. Washington, D. C., 1984.

Grolier, M. J., and J. W. Bingham. *Geologic Map and Sections of Parts of Grant, Adams and Franklin Counties, Washington.* Miscellaneous Geologic Investigations Map I-589, U. S. Geological Survey. Washington D. C., 1971.

——*Geology of Parts of Grant, Adams, and Franklin Counties, East-Central Washington.* Washington. Department of Natural Resources, Division of Geology and Earth Resources, Bulletin no. 71. Olympia, 1978.

Hunting, Marshall, T., W. A. G. Bennett, Vaughn E. Livingston, and Wayne S. Moen. *Geologic Map of Washington.* Washington. Division of Mines and Geology. Olympia, 1961.

Kurten, Bjorn. *How To Deep-Freeze A Mammoth.* New York: Columbia University Press, 1986.

Mackin, J. Hoover, and Allan S. Carey. *Origin of Cascade Landscapes.* Washington. Division of Mines and Geology Information Circular 40 (1965).

McKee, Bates. *Cascadia: The Geologic Evolution of the Pacific Northwest.* New York: McGraw-Hill Book Co., 1972.

Neff, George E. "Columbia Basin Project" In Vol. 1 of *Engineering Geology in Washington.* Washington. Division of Geology and Earth Resources, Bulletin no. 78. Olympia, 1989: 535–563.

Rigg, George B. *Peat Resources of Washington.* Washington. Division of Mines and Geology, Bulletin no. 44. Olympia, 1958.

Schminke, Hans-Ulrich. *Petrology, Paleocurrents, and Stratigraphy of the Ellensburg Formation and Interbedded Yakima Basalt Flows in South Central Washington.* Ph.D diss., John Hopkins University. 1964.

Shelton, John S. *Geology Illustrated.* San Francisco: W. H. Freeman and Company, 1966.

Smiley, Charles J. *The Ellensburg Flora of Washington.* University of California Publications in Geological Sciences. Vol. 35, No. 3. University of California Press. Berkeley, 1963: 159–275.

United States Department of Interior. U. S. Geological Survey. *The Channeled Scablands of Eastern Washington: The Geologic Story of the Spokane Flood.* Washington, D. C., 1973.

Waitt, Richard B. "Scores of Gigantic, Successively Smaller Lake Missoula Floods Through Channeled Scabland and Columbia Valley." From: Swanson, D. A., and Haugerud, R. A. editors, *Geologic Field Trips in the Pacific Northwest: 1994 Geological Society of America Annual Meeting.* Chapter 1K

Webster, G. D., Victor R. Baker, and Carl E. Gustafson. *Channeled Scablands in S. E. Washington, A Roadlog via Spokane-Coulee City-Vantage-Washtucna-Lewiston-Pullman.* Field Guide No. 2. Cordilleran Section, 72nd Annual Meeting. Geological Society of America, 1976.

Index

A

Alkali Lake 28, 33
anticline 32, 51, 57, 65, 80, 85

B

Babcock Ridge 9, 57, 61, 67
Banks Lake 13, 18, 20, 22, 25-26, 30, 39-40, 43
bar 10-11, 21, 40, 43, 47-48, 52, 57-59, 67-68, 83, 85
basalt 1-6, 11-12, 17-18, 20-23, 26-27, 29, 30-32, 36, 39-40, 47-48, 51, 55, 57-58, 61, 66, 68, 71-72, 76, 80, 83, 85-86
bed load deposits 28, 68, 71, 85
Beezley Hills 4, 6, 45, 48, 57
Beverly 62
Billy Clapp Lake 30, 40-41
Blue Lake 27-28
Bretz, J Harlen 8, 9, 89

C

caliche 5, 7, 36, 40, 61-62, 67, 71, 76, 85
Canals
    East Low Canal 30, 55, 68, 76
    Feeder Canal 30
    Main Canal 30, 39-41
    West Canal 30, 57, 62
Columbia Basin Irrigation Project 13, 28, 30, 31, 39, 55, 68, 79, 87
Columbia Plateau 2-4, 10, 61, 86, 89
Columbia River 1, 5-13, 17-18, 28, 30, 35, 39-40, 48, 57-59, 61-62, 65-67, 76, 80, 83-84, 86, 89
Corfu 71
Coulee City 4, 7, 17, 23, 39-41, 43, 90
County Roads
    Dodson Road 71
    Grand Coulee Hill Road 35
    H SE 79, 81
    North Frontage Road 66
    Pinto Ridge Road 39-40

    R NE 36
    Stratford Road 55
    V NE 36
    50 NE 35-36
Crab Creek 6, 8-9, 12-13, 41, 43, 48-49, 51-52, 55, 65, 68, 72, 79, 83
Crescent Bar 12, 57-59

D

Drumheller Channels 8-9, 11-12, 48, 66, 72, 79-80
Dry Coulee 40, 51
Dry Falls 11, 23, 25-29, 32, 39-40
Dry Falls Interpretive Center 25, 27
dunes 48, 62, 68, 75

E

Electric City 18, 20
Ephrata 4, 9, 12, 30, 39, 44-48, 57, 61-62
erratic 11, 46, 81, 86
Evergreen Ridge 7, 9, 61, 66

F

fossils 3, 6, 40, 75
Frenchman Hills 4, 6, 13, 30, 62, 65, 71, 80

G

Ginkgo Petrified Forest 65, 69
Grand Coulee 1-2, 4, 6, 8-13, 15, 17-18, 20-23, 26-32, 35-36, 40-41, 43, 45-48, 58-59, 62, 67
granite 1-2, 11, 17, 21, 46, 86
gravel bar 10-11, 21, 43, 48, 51, 67, 83

H

hanging valleys 11, 21-22
Hartline 35-36, 39, 43, 48
Hiawatha Valley 67-68
High Hill 26, 29, 40

I

Interstate Freeway 90 62, 65-66, 68-69

irrigation 13, 15, 28, 30, 39-40, 55, 62, 67, 79, 87

L

Lake Lenore 11, 26-30
Lake Missoula 7-9, 11, 18, 30, 59, 89
Lake Roosevelt 35
lava 1-6, 11-12, 17-18, 20-23, 25-27, 29-30, 32, 33, 40, 58, 65, 71, 76, 80, 85-87
Lind Coulee 6-7, 13, 75-76
loess 6-7, 9, 12, 36, 41, 43, 48, 51, 55, 57, 62, 67-68, 71, 86

M

Mae Valley 67- 68
Mattawa 83
Missoula Floods 8, 13, 18, 45-46, 66, 80, 86, 89-90
Moses Coulee 8-9, 36, 45
Moses Lake 8, 10-12, 30, 41, 43-46, 48-49, 54-55, 65-69, 75, 79

N

North Dam 18
Northrup Canyon 21

O

O'Sullivan Dam 79-80

P

Park Lake 26-28
Pasco 2, 4, 6, 12-13, 43, 46, 59, 62, 83, 86
petrified 3, 27, 40, 65
pillow basalt 27, 40, 71, 86
Pinto Dam 40-41
Pinto Ridge 26, 39-40
Potholes Reservoir 62, 67-68, 79
Priest Rapids Dam 83

Q

Quincy 4, 6-7, 9, 12-13, 30, 41, 43, 45, 48, 57-58, 61-62, 65-67, 79

R

Ringold Formation 6, 12, 30, 40, 46-47, 66-67, 71-72, 75-76, 84, 86
ripple marks 10-11, 52, 58-59, 86
Rocky Coulee 6, 41
Rocky Ford Creek 12-13, 47-48, 52
Royal City 4, 43, 71-72

S

Saddle Mountains 4, 6, 30, 71-72, 83, 84
Sanitarium Lake 31
scablands 7, 11, 17-18, 35, 39, 41, 52, 68, 86, 89-90
Schawana 8, 48, 83
Sentinel Gap 83-84
slack water 43, 69, 76
Smyrna 71
Soap Lake 4, 8, 11-12, 18, 25-26, 28, 30-32, 44-47, 51
South Dam 39
State Highways
    State Highway 17 25, 28, 32, 45-48, 52, 75-76, 79
    State Highway 174 35
    State Highway 24 83-84
    State Highway 243 83
    State Highway 26 71, 81
    State Highway 262 79, 80-81
    State Highway 28 39, 45, 47-48, 51, 55, 57, 61
    State Highway 281 61-63
    State Highway 282 45, 47-49
    State Highway 283 61-62
Steamboat Rock 9, 11-12, 17, 20-21, 25, 36, 46
Stratford 39, 40-41, 51-55
Summer Falls 30, 40-41
Sun Lakes State Park 26

T

talus 22-23, 27, 29, 58-59, 87

U

U. S. Highway 2 7, 25, 36, 39, 43

V

varves 18, 28, 87

W

Wallula Gap 62, 83
Wanapum Lake 65
Warden 13, 30, 68, 76
Winchester Wasteway 57, 62, 67